A SC

Lisa Fielding's reputation as a scarlet woman was really only media lies, but Alex Andreas believed them. Nevertheless he wanted her and he was too used to getting what he wanted for Lisa to resist . . .

A SCARLET WOMAN

BY

MARGARET PARGETER

MILLS & BOON LIMITED
15–16 BROOK'S MEWS
LONDON W1A 1DR

*First published in Great Britain 1986
by Mills & Boon Limited*

© *Margaret Pargeter 1986*

*Australian copyright 1986
Philippine copyright 1986
This edition 1986*

ISBN 0 263 75308 5

*Set in Monophoto Times 10 on 10½ pt.
01–0386 – 59120*

*Made and printed in Great Britain by
Richard Clay (The Chaucer Press) Ltd,
Bungay, Suffolk*

CHAPTER ONE

LISA FIELDING aged twenty-two, a slender blonde, recently widowed, licked dry lips nervously as she tried to find sufficient courage to speak.

'My husband left me the island, Mr Andreas, and it was his last wish that I should come to Greece to see you.'

The dark Greek sitting opposite her nodded abruptly. 'I have only just learned of your husband's death, Mrs Fielding, otherwise I should have come to you.'

Why? Lisa wondered as she acknowledged soberly, 'I should have appreciated that, Mr Andreas. I had no desire to fly all the way from London to Athens but as it was Philip's last request, I felt I couldn't refuse.'

'Quite,' Alex Andreas broke in smoothly. 'I can only apologise for what appears to have been a regrettable breakdown in communications. Your husband promised I should be informed without delay of his demise, because of the island, but he obviously forgot to make the necessary arrangements.'

Lisa frowned, finding his constant reference to the island difficult to understand. They were talking stiltedly, in the manner of two strangers extremely wary of each other, but apart from Andreas's interest in the island nothing else was immediately apparent.

Her blue eyes darkening, she suggested uncertainly, 'You appear to have been involved, in some way, with my property, Mr Andreas.'

Alex Andreas's black eyes sharpened but he didn't reply for a moment and the ensuing silence did nothing for Lisa's nerves. He was, according to Edward Sterne, Philip's solicitor, one of the world's richest men and, from what she had seen, so far, she saw no reason to

5

doubt it. If these offices and the suit he was wearing were a reflection of his wealth, he must be worth a huge fortune! Lisa stared at him, trying not to be impressed as she noted how the dark grey cloth of his suit was expertly tailored to enhance his tall, lean figure. He had a body, she was forced to admit, which might be equally impressive without it!

Drawing a quick breath, Lisa hoped the heat in her cheeks didn't betray her wayward thoughts. The trauma of the past weeks, as well as the last four years, must have deranged her slightly if she could think so intimately of another man with her husband scarcely cold in his grave.

Alex Andreas was impressive, though. At thirty-six, in the prime of life, he had a splendid physique and rugged good looks to match. His manner was forceful, his vitality overpowering—he wasn't a man who would ever go unnoticed. Again, according to Edward, Andreas was a bachelor, so there would be no wife to soften the ruthless lines of his face. But though he might be unmarried, Lisa saw something in the sensuous hardness of his mouth which made her suspect he was far from celibate.

In a moment of irrational panic, born of feelings she couldn't define, Lisa wished he would get on with whatever it was they had to discuss then she could leave.

As if in response to the urgent appeal in her eyes, Alex Andreas stopped meditating and asked coolly, 'Have you ever visited this island your husband left you?'

'No.'

'Had you any idea it even existed before Philip died?'

Bewildered, Lisa shook her head. Why did she feel she was being attacked? Edward had warned her that he believed there was some mystery attached to the island. He had, in fact, felt so strongly about it that he had wanted to accompany her to Greece himself, an offer she had instinctively declined. Now she wondered if she had been wise. Alex Andreas was clearly a force to be reckoned with and if she didn't agree with the proposition she sensed he was about to make, she wasn't sure how he might react.

'I knew nothing of the island until a day or two ago,' she confessed, rather than lie.

The eyes she met with an upwards sweep of long lashes, glinted with swiftly concealed triumph. 'Then I hardly think we need go into further details, Mrs Fielding. It might be sufficient to say that the island once belonged to me and I wish to buy it back. Your husband actually promised that the island should revert to me on his death but neither of us could, of course, foresee he would marry a girl young enough to be his granddaughter, and you will, understandably, require all the money you can lay hands on to see you comfortably through the long years you still have ahead of you. I already have the papers drawn up ready for you to sign immediately, and I'm sure you will find the terms extremely generous.'

Lisa opened her mouth then closed it again angrily. Perhaps Alex Andreas couldn't be blamed for assuming she wished to sell the island but he was taking a great deal for granted. Nor did she care for the underlying insolence in his voice when he spoke of her marriage. The age difference between herself and Philip was surely no business of his! Hadn't she suffered enough because of it, over the past four years. What right had he to judge her? He may have been Philip's friend but she hadn't known of Andreas's existence until the will had been read and she certainly had no intention of confiding in him that though she had been Philip's wife, she was still as untouched as she had been on the day she was married.

The island, however, was another thing. She hadn't been impressed on first learning of it, yet, on the way here, she had began dreaming of golden days spent on

sun-soaked beaches. A feeling of quiet elation had
gripped her as, for the first time in her life, she
contemplated being entirely free to do as she liked. She
knew that even thinking of living on the island might be
totally unrealistic but she certainly wasn't going to part
with it before exploring all its possibilities.

'I'm sorry, Mr Andreas,' she replied, adopting his
distant tones. 'I'm afraid I'm not ready to make a
decision about the island at this stage. Money isn't that
important to me, despite the long years I have ahead of
me,' she emphasised drily, 'to make me feel I must take
a step I might live to regret.'

To her surprise, Andreas sprang to his feet and
walked over to the window where he stood gazing out
over the teeming city. Lisa followed the powerful
movement of his hips, the set of broad shoulders, the
arrogant lines of his head but looked away swiftly as he
turned forbiddingly.

'Can you give me one good reason for wishing to
keep the island?'

'Not a logical one,' she admitted frankly.

'Let's hear the illogical ones then,' he demanded
abrasively.

Lisa flinched but met his sarcastic glance courage-
ously. She felt like a molehill fighting a mountain. He
was trying to bulldoze her into doing what he wanted.
Next he would probably try charm. She would need all
her wits about her to successfully thwart him. It
irritated her further that she wasn't altogether sure that
this was what she wanted.

'Islands have an appeal of their own, Mr Andreas,'
she began deliberately. 'Most people dream of owning
one but for the vast majority it remains a dream. When
Edward, Mr Sterne, first told me about the island, I
scarcely took it in, but, on the plane, coming here, I
thought how lovely it would be to spend some time
there . . .'

Raising an impatient hand, he interrupted

curtly. 'That sounds all very fine, Mrs Fielding, but, in reality, Enos falls far short of what you appear to expect. It is extremely bare and isolated while the house, which hasn't been lived in for years, is little more than a ruin. It is certainly not habitable.'

Dismay clutched Lisa's stomach but she replied evenly enough. 'I have only your word for this, Mr Andreas.'

His mouth tightened and, as he made a visible attempt to control his temper, Lisa realised her former suspicions were proving correct. Andreas was angry but determined to hide it in order to get his own way. The forced smile on his mouth was so predictable, she almost smiled herself.

'Naturally you doubt my word,' he conceded with gentle irony, 'but there are plenty of reliable sources where you can check everything I've said. Apart from this, a beautiful young woman would attract all kinds of questionable attention, should she attempt to live on Enos alone. Unless this doesn't deter you, Mrs Fielding, I should advise you to forget it.'

Lisa bristled, though, like him she hid her anger. He enjoyed having digs at her character, whether he realised it or not. It made her wonder, as she had wondered so often and so bitterly in the past, at the cruelty of human nature. Like many others, Andreas believed she had married Philip Fielding for his money, while nothing could be farther from the truth. Andreas must have known of Philip's marriage from the beginning and was so ready to condemn her that, in turn, she was more than ready to defy him.

Composing her features into lines of rather naïve innocence, she addressed the man stalking about in front of her. 'I could put the island on the open market, Mr Andreas.'

She saw the knuckles of his hands go white as they clenched but by the time she reached his face he was all mocking charm. 'Why not take a look at what I'm offering?' he suggested smoothly, in his perfect English. 'It's a great deal more than you would ever get from anyone else.'

Reaching for a paper lying on his desk, he swivelled it around, thrusting it under her nose so she could read the figures printed on it. Lisa glanced at it reluctantly then gasped. Edward, realising Andreas might make an offer, had given her some indication of what he considered Enos was worth. He was an acknowledged authority on such matters but this was more than even he had envisaged. If Andreas was willing to pay this much for Enos he must want it very badly. Not surprisingly Lisa's curiosity was aroused.

Raising startled eyes to the dark face hovering above her, she enquired blankly, 'Why are you so eager to part with this kind of money for what you admit yourself is not a viable proposition?'

He laughed mirthlessly. 'There is no mineral wealth or hidden potential, if that is what you mean, Mrs Fielding. I am not trying to pull a fast one, in any way. I want it for personal reasons you wouldn't understand.'

'Try me?' she invited.

'I'd rather not.'

'Well, I'd rather not sell, Mr Andreas,' she retorted recklessly. 'And, like you, I don't feel it necessary to be more explicit.'

The sudden biting anger in his eyes caused her to draw back. He wasn't used to defiance, the tight control he exercised over his patience slipped. 'You're holding out for more?'

'No . . .'

'Don't lie,' he snapped. 'Trust Philip to tie himself to a mercenary little bitch like yourself. In a way it serves him right, but how much did he have to pay you to revive his jaded appetites? Over the odds, I bet!'

Lisa felt her face grow white as she stumbled to her feet. 'You have no right to say such things!' she exclaimed. 'My marriage is none of your business and I don't have to listen to your insults.'

'I'm sorry.' The anger in the black eyes died or was controlled. Lisa couldn't be sure which but she suspected the latter. 'It was inexcusable of me to express such thoughts aloud.'

No worse than thinking them—Lisa looked at him bitterly. 'Like everyone else, you jump to conclusions.'

'The wrong ones?'

He was twisting her words to suit his vindictive mood. He may have apologised but he still believed she had married Philip for what she could get out of him. Yet why should she explain the circumstances of her marriage to him or anyone? Like many he probably enjoyed gossip and unkind fabrication better than the truth. Her refusal to sell the island immediately rankled, she could see that, which would partly account for his cynicism, but not getting his own way might be good for a man like Andreas occasionally!

'I don't think,' she replied aloofly, 'my marriage is something we need discuss.'

'I agree,' he responded suavely. 'I'm only interested in the island.'

'It's difficult,' she smiled faintly, 'when two people want the same thing.'

His mouth twisted cynically. 'About the only place such a situation can be resolved amicably is in bed.'

'Mr Andreas!' She glared, with scarlet cheeks. She knew she was overreacting. He was a man of extreme sophistication to whom such remarks would be common place, but she just wished to get away from him. Half turning, she muttered stiffly, 'If you'll excuse me, I'll get back to my hotel.'

He was beside her in a flash, moving swiftly for so big a man, grasping hold of her when she would have run. Feeling pain in her shoulders, Lisa winced. She was a little short of medium height and too thin. Andreas's harsh hands hurt her badly.

He took no notice when her blue eyes clouded with anguish, if anything his grip tightened. 'You haven't seen Enos yet,' he exclaimed. 'I think it would be better if we went there at once, so you can see for yourself how it could never be of any use to you.'

'Mr—Andreas!' she breathed. 'I have no intention of going anywhere at the moment. I'm tired. I went straight from the airport to my hotel, and from there I came straight here. I shall visit the island, I promise you, but when I do, I'm quite capable of making my own arrangements.'

He muttered something under his breath in Greek which she was sure was a curse. He was getting angry again, she could feel the force of it transmitting through his hands, invading her pores. It aroused a peculiar sensation deep within her which she had never experienced before. Swallowing, she tried to compose herself, putting such irrational feelings down to nerves. 'Would you please let go of me?' she exclaimed unevenly.

'Why should I?' he grated, clearly incensed. 'I'm giving you a choice. Either you come to Enos willingly or I take you there by force.'

'You couldn't!' she gasped, almost as furious as he was. 'You wouldn't dare . . .'

'You're being very unwise, taking that attitude with me,' he snapped. 'I'll give you one more chance.'

'You have police in Greece,' she snapped back.

He merely laughed.

About to defy him again, she paused. She might not help matters by making him angrier than he already was, and if she did as he asked, what had she to lose? It suddenly occurred to her that getting to the island by herself could prove an expensive business. It could be smarter in the long run, to let Andreas take her there— and she could still refuse to sell it to him. If this infuriated him afresh, he could only call her a few more names, there was nothing else he could do.

'I don't seem to be in a position to refuse,' she sighed, pretending to be intimidated by his threatening tone. 'But must we go today?'

'The sooner the better, I think.' He regarded her so suspiciously that Lisa knew he suspected she might change her mind if he allowed her the least leeway. 'My secretary will bring you coffee,' he went on, a little more amiably, 'while I make the necessary arangements with my assistant.'

He left without supplying any further information, leaving Lisa to sip the coffee she didn't want and wonder anxiously what she had let herself in for. Only time would tell whether she had been wise in agreeing to go to Enos with him. For her own peace of mind she didn't dwell on the methods he might have used if she had continued to hold out against him.

Ten minutes later he returned and fifteen minutes after that they left Athens in a helicopter piloted by a young man he introduced to her as Paul Erastus. Lisa presumed, on listening to their conversation, that he must be the assistant Andreas had mentioned.

As they left the city, Andreas pointed out some famous landmarks and, after discussing the ones he felt she ought to see, while she was here, he asked several questions about her journey from England. He was so charming that she wondered if, for some mysterious reason, he was trying to give Paul the impression that they were on much better terms than they actually were. Paul had looked at her quickly, with guarded interest, but although he spoke English almost as well as his employer, he'd had very little to say for himself.

It wasn't until Andreas leant forward to speak to him again that the fears Andreas had succeeded in partly lulling returned. She began to feel she had acted too hastily in giving in to him so easily. Ought she not to have insisted on postponing this trip until tomorrow? If she had been determined enough, he surely couldn't have refused, and it would have given her a chance to ring Edward. What did she know of Andreas other than the few things Edward had told her? Edward obviously didn't know everything and she had stepped into Andreas's web like a witless fly!

As he turned back to her, an alarming thought suddenly struck her like a blow. 'You don't intend keeping me on the island until I agree to let you have it?' she gasped.

Warmth faded from the black eyes as he shook his head. 'Nothing as barbaric,' he said. 'I want the island but I hope to acquire it in a civilised manner, without the publicity that holding you prisoner could bring. I like to achieve my objectives with a minimum of fuss.'

He really was too much! Lisa lowered her lashes, feeling a return of her initial dislike. He'd be lucky if she ever agreed to sell him the island. Maybe his high-handed methods had served him well up to now, but it might do him no harm to learn, as lesser mortals frequently did, that success couldn't always be guaranteed.

As her silent antagonism appeared to be having little effect on his granite-like resilience, she directed her anxious attention towards the sea and the land they were fast approaching. The sea was blue, the beautiful glittering blue of the Aegean, but Enos looked wild. It seemed to be composed of barren rock and greeny brown hills. Lisa held her breath as they seemed to hurtle towards it then paused like a hawk above a helpless bird before swooping to pounce on it gently.

'Here we are,' said Andreas, smiling blandly.

Lisa, busy trying to recover her shattered equilibrium, gazed mutinously in front of her. Did he expect her to jump up and thank him, to dance with glee? She took refuge in icy silence, again regretting agreeing to come here so hastily.

Nevertheless, she submitted to being lifted out of the aircraft to the ground. Andreas was still smiling and somehow, against her will, she found herself smiling back at him. It was then that she really felt, for the first time, the full impact of his charm and, unconsciously reacting to it, her eyes darkened.

All realisation of his charm fled, however, when she heard him shout to his assistant. 'Throw out the gear, Paul, and return for us first thing in the morning. Don't forget I have an appointment.'

As he moved her aside so he could catch the two bulky sacks Paul dumped out after them, she wondered distractedly what was in them. And what had Andreas meant when he'd told Paul to return in the morning? Feeling suddenly terrified, she attempted to reach the helicopter but Andreas merely caught hold of her again, to allow Paul to take off. Lisa watched him soaring into the sky with terrible suspicion in her heart that she had just lost her last link with civilisation.

Andreas was watching her, rather than the helicopter's dwindling outline. Becoming aware of this, Lisa was aroused to swift fury.

'Why have you done this?' she raged, eyes flashing. 'I can't stay here with you. I thought we'd be having a quick look around and leaving immediately.'

'You can't see Enos in five minutes.' He shrugged.

'You're evading the issue,' she retorted. 'Unless,' she paused hopefully, 'there's a hotel, or inn somewhere?'

'There's nothing like that,' he replied coolly. 'The island is deserted. I thought I'd told you?'

'I didn't think you meant that deserted!' she said sharply.

He looked at her indignant face with faint amusement. 'Many would consider this quite an adventure. A lot of women would give much to be in your shoes, right now, Mrs Fielding, but I don't intend taking advantage of the situation. Whether this disappoints you or not, I have no idea. As far as I'm concerned, you wanted to see the island and this takes time, which is why we are staying.'

Lisa glared at him through her tears. 'I'd as soon

associate with a rat! I know I wanted to come here but I could have hired a boat. Nothing on earth,' she choked, 'could justify the action you've taken.'

'We've already gone into that,' he replied curtly. 'And, until Paul returns to collect us, I'd advise you to guard your tongue.'

Her eyes blazed. She had tolerated all she was going to tolerate from him! 'If Paul isn't returning until tomorrow, I'd like to ask a few questions.'

'Such as?'

She stared at him, her delicate features set rebelliously, though she realised the futility of fighting him. 'Such as where do we sleep?'

'Thinking of that already, are we?' The anger in his dark eyes was replaced by mockery. 'You'll be quite comfortable, I assure you.'

Lisa counted ten but it took two more before she was able to reply evenly. 'How can I be comfortable if there isn't a hotel? You said the house is in ruins.'

'There are sleeping bags in the sacks.'

'Sleeping bags!' she exclaimed. 'You must be mad!' Rubbing the wrist he had grabbed to keep her out of the way of the helicopter, she felt like killing the swarthy skinned Greek standing in front of her. 'Do you realise,' she continued irrationally, 'I've been wearing the same clothing since last night!'

'Clothes are of no importance here.' His insolent glance slid over her and she wished she had kept her mouth shut. 'There's fresh water by the house, where you may wash if you wish. Surely, for one evening, this should suffice?'

'Well, that's the least of my worries,' she supposed, then went bright red as he couldn't possibly mistake her meaning.

'You think I'm going to pounce on you as soon as the sun goes down?' Glancing derisively towards the horizon, he smiled tauntingly. 'From the looks of it, you shouldn't have long to wait.'

'I'd be overestimating my own attraction if I believed you had designs on me,' Lisa retorted, ignoring the frightened beat of her heart.

'You couldn't do that,' he replied coolly, his black eyes travelling over her again. 'You are unusually beautiful, even if for some reason you choose to adopt a prim image. You keep your hair tightly bound, your skirts long, but I have eyes and imagination, my dear, as well as some knowledge of your reputation. For the duration of your stay here, though, you have nothing to fear from me. I wish to gain your trust which, in turn, will, I hope, help to convince you, you can safely sell the island to me.'

Lisa fumed at the nerve of the man! He threw out compliments then laced them with abuse which he appeared to think she should accept. 'In bringing me here, like this, don't you think you've destroyed any possibility of that?' she asked.

His eyes hardened and he said curtly, 'I'm a busy man, Mrs Fielding. If I take short cuts, I know what I'm doing. In this case, I'm saving us both time. Maybe I have been ruthless but you were so determined not to co-operate that I was forced to resort to doing this.'

'I didn't come to Greece to fight you,' she protested, clenching her hands. 'If you had been patient, I'm sure we could have reached an agreement.'

He smiled thinly. 'After you had wrung every possible drachma out of me.'

Lisa looked about her, feeling hunted. Repeatedly he accused her of being mercenary and just as frequently she denied it. She refused to go on wasting her breath! Instinctively she knew she didn't have to fear he would assault her—the island would be far more important to him than any transient pleasure he might get from possessing her. But he was impatient, so full of baleful frustration that she wouldn't give in to him immediately, and she realised it might take a lot of strength to withstand him.

'I've told you,' she said sharply, 'that your high-handed methods don't impress me.'

'I can be reasonable,' he replied, an aggrieved expression on his face, 'but not if you won't be.'

'I don't think I've been anything else,' she retorted sharply. 'And if you are determined to mend your ways, you can start by showing me the island. As I am here, albeit unwillingly, I may as well see what there is to see, and, if you don't mind, where I am to sleep?'

His mouth tightened at her haughty tones, which he didn't guess hid the ever present panic she tried to conceal from him. With deadly accuracy he hit back. 'I don't care for your attitude, Mrs Fielding, but I suppose, being an old man's darling, you are used to being spoiled. Did you find it a lot more rewarding than being a younger man's slave?'

Lisa stifled a furious gasp. Andreas had no regard for her feelings. He certainly knew how to hurt. Bitterly she reflected, he couldn't know how much! Throwing him a stony glance, which he shrugged off with complete indifference, she followed him numbly over the rough terrain.

Stumbling along a path she couldn't see for angry tears, but which he seemed familiar with, she thought how Philip would have laughed if he could have overheard their conversation. He had married her but it was another woman who had been his darling It was Philip who had reaped the advantages from their marriage while for Lisa there had been few rewards, if any. Contrary to what Andreas thought, she had been left nothing apart from an old terraced house in a poorer part of London, and an allowance barely enough to keep her alive. And Enos, of course. However, she had one thing now that she valued above all else—her freedom, which she would be reluctant to part with again!

Yet for all her bitter and long standing determination to have nothing more to do with men, her eyes, when she knuckled them dry, clung to Andreas's tall figure as he strode in front of her carrying the two sacks which Paul had dropped from the helicopter. She still didn't know what was in them but he carried them easily on his broad shoulders. In spite of his wealth, which many men might have used as an excuse for soft living, he was obviously in superb physical condition. His strong legs and powerful thighs propelled him forward in long strides, soon leaving Lisa behind.

As if becoming aware of the distance he was putting between them, he paused and looked back. 'Soft, are you, Mrs Fielding?' he laughed. 'If you had married a younger man he might have kept you more resilient.'

Angrily she caught up with him. 'I know what you are hinting at,' she snapped. 'But if you don't have any respect for, me at least have some for the dead.'

'Philip Fielding never did anything to earn my respect,' he muttered harshly.

'You can't blame me for that!' she retorted heatedly. 'How many times do I have to tell you, if you want to buy Enos from me, you aren't going about it the right way.'

His hard lips parted on a taunting flash of white teeth. 'Not even for the sake of the island, Mrs Fielding, can I be bribed against speaking my mind.'

Lisa's soft mouth pursed, but she decided she wouldn't be provoked any further. Lifting her chin scornfully, she walked past him, ignoring his amusement. Not that she could blame him for being amused, she thought morosely. If he regarded her as a fool, she only had herself to blame! Before she had married Philip, she had often acted impulsively, but she had believed that the ensuing years had corrected this fault in her. She hadn't recognised it when it had surfaced again, bringing her to Greece when she should have known better, driving her to seeking out a man she would have been wiser to have kept at a distance. In future she would listen to Edward's advice, however dull and unwarranted it may seem. It could be less painful!

They rounded a corner between clumps of wild olives and other trees. Lisa, absorbed in rueful thoughts, wasn't prepared for the house which appeared suddenly in front of them. Halting abruptly, she blinked in amazement. What must once have been a large, sprawling villa, was now little more than a ruin.

Lifting stunned eyes to Andreas's grim face, she realised he had been speaking the truth when he had warned her about it. It came to her that he wasn't a man to demean himself by lying over something like this. If he deceived it would be by omission . . .

'Why?' she breathed, unable to believe that Philip, for all his faults, would willingly have let this happen to anything he owned.

'You may well ask, Mrs Fielding.'

Andreas spoke so coldly she found her eyes widening. She saw he had gone quite pale and again her curiosity was aroused. She decided, there and then, that she wouldn't let Enos go before it was satisfied. It must have to do with Philip, anyway, she excused herself.

His face set darkly, Andreas walked on. Lisa followed nervously. Her first dismay on witnessing the destruction of such a beautiful house was swiftly replaced by a feeling of odd excitement. Something about Andreas challenged her—she had only just become conscious of it. It could be the way he looked at her but she could feel her emotions coming to life as they hadn't done in years. He filled her with anger and resentment but there was something else which brought the blood rushing to her temples, making her whole body aware of it.

On closer inspection, the house, after reaching it, did nothing to change her first impression of it. The roof had caved in, the wind whistled ghoulishly through broken windows, unhinged doors swung drunkenly and creaked.

Lisa swallowed a thickness that had collected on her tongue and found herself asking, in a voice that sounded nothing like her own, 'Didn't Philip like it?'

'Don't you think there is enough evidence to prove he didn't?' Andreas said sarcastically.

'Why didn't you do something?' she persisted hollowly.

'One doesn't repair another man's property,' he retorted harshly. 'Even to come here would have been trespassing.'

'You are doing it today,' she reminded him.

'Circumstances have changed.'

'Because the new owner is a woman?'

'Are you?' He turned on her in a way she was growing familiar with and finding increasingly disconcerting. 'You haven't shown many womanly attributes so far. If I didn't know differently I'd say you were little more than a child.'

She lifted her glance from the house and stared into his eyes. 'Whatever your personal opinion of me, I'm not a child, and there's no need to treat me like one, Mr Andreas.'

'Is that an invitation?' he asked.

Heat invaded Lisa's cheeks but she managed to retort coldly, 'Certainly not.'

'I quite agree,' Andreas surprised her by acceding curtly. 'I brought you here to show you the island and discuss the sale of it, nothing else.'

As Lisa hadn't changed her mind over selling, she hurriedly side-stepped the issue by enquiring shortly where she might wash. 'A meal, I realise, will be out of the question, but I'd like to feel clean.'

Fury darkened his eyes so she knew he was aware of her continuing evasion, but he didn't argue. 'There's a well over there.' Raising his hand, he pointed to a spot a hundred yards from where they were standing. 'The indoor taps don't work anymore, and the condition of the house makes it scarcely safe to enter.'

'A—well?'

His mouth twisted at the suspicion in her eyes. 'Don't be alarmed,' he scorned. 'I shan't push you down it. It's really a spring, too shallow to drown anyone, and while you are busy removing the imaginary grime, I'll make a start on the meal you are worrying about.'

She wasn't worrying about it. Her appetite had gone but she merely turned with a shrug. She could have done with a cup of tea but that was all. She had more important things than a missed meal to think about. If she was clever she might be able to elude Andreas and escape from him.

'Don't take too long,' he called, 'or I'll come after you.' And Lisa's newly born hopes fled as she realised he meant it.

CHAPTER TWO

THE well, as Andreas had said, was little more than a shallow depression in the rock. It filled from a crevice in the rough ground above it, the overflow running down the cliff face into the sea.

With a resigned sigh, Lisa removed her cotton blouson and dipped her fingers in the clear, sparkling water then splashed it over her face. Its coolness revived her until she remembered she had nothing to dry herself with. While she was wondering what she could use for a towel, she was startled to find one thrust in her hands.

'You forgot this,' growled Andreas's deep voice, as she blinked water from her eyes in embarrassment.

'Th-thank you,' she stammered, feeling so disconcerted she was grateful he didn't linger. With the moisture gone from her eyes, she was just in time to see him striding back the way he had come. Something intimidating in the set of his wide shoulders made her shiver. She might have got over her first fear of him but he was still able to fill her stomach full of nervous tension.

There was also a peculiar tightness in her head. Attempting to relieve it, she released the heavy braids of her hair and ran her fingers through it. As the heavy mass of it rippled across her face, she pushed it back impatiently. She had worn it coiled at her nape during her marriage, to make her look older, but now that Philip was gone, she supposed this was no longer necessary.

Refreshed, if still far from reassured, Lisa picked up her blouson and stepped nearer the cliff edge to glance down, Her breath caught at the drop her curious eyes encountered. The cliffs fell sheer to the sea. There was

23

no sign of the beautiful Aegean sands she had envisaged.

Enos resembled a fortress more than anything else. The cliffs continued as far as the eye could see, with no obvious place for a boat to land. There must be a harbour somewhere but an inexperienced person like herself, or even an experienced one unfamiliar with the coast and its currents, might be smashed to pieces on the rocks before they ever got near it.

Disappointment clouding her blue eyes, Lisa turned from the perilous coastline to gaze at the ruins of the house then on to the desolate acres around it. Even if the problem of getting here could be solved, the pittance Philip had left her wouldn't be sufficient to repair the house. Andreas was right. In believing she could come and live here, she had been dreaming of the impossible.

Nevertheless, she was determined not to acquaint him with her change of mind immmediately. First she would go home and consult Edward. Andreas would be angry at the delay but she couldn't feel sorry for him. After the way he had treated her today, didn't he deserve to suffer—if only from frustration? She would eventually sell Enos to him, as Philip had clearly meant him to have it, but in her own time and at her own price!

Frowning absently, she let her eyes wander, despite the knowledge Andreas might come seeking her any minute. If he maintained his stubborn silence, she might never learn why Philip had wanted him to have the island. Even Edward, who had known everything there was to know about Philip Fielding, had no idea—just as he hadn't known either how Philip had acquired Enos in the first place, or why he had decreed she shouldn't be told about it until three months after his death. If Andreas wouldn't tell her, and he seemed the only person who could, she wouldn't beg, but she would keep him guessing and waiting until he did!

A decision arrived at, at last, Lisa retraced her steps to the house. To her surprise she found Andreas kneeling over a charcoal fire, grilling lamb chops. On the other side of the fire was a jugful of hot soup. He had changed from his suit into a pair of jeans and she felt her breath falter at the difference they made to his appearance. Dressed like this, with a matching blue shirt open at the neck, his dark skin looked even darker while the tight fit of his pants over his thighs and waist, did nothing but emphasise his hard masculinity.

As she moved nervously nearer, he glanced up, eyes narrowing as they rested on her flowing mane of hair. Rising slowly to his feet he reached out and touched it.

'Beautiful!' he breathed. 'So pale.'

Her lips curved in a smile she hadn't intended. 'Greeks are supposed to like fair women.'

He continued to stare at her thoughtfully. 'I've had no particular preference until now.'

Her smile widened with increasing confidence. He was flattering her with one thing in mind but she needn't be afraid he would go too far. His fear of losing the island would save her, as long as she kept him guessing. He may be aware of what she was up to but he couldn't prove anything. And he couldn't despise her more than he did already!

Yet, as she gazed into the black eyes fixed on hers, she knew a moment's misgiving. If she goaded Andreas too far, he would make a deadly enemy. Edward had warned her he wasn't a man to be played with and Edward always knew what he was talking about.

'You don't realise his power,' he had said. 'Andreas can make men or break them with a flick of his little finger.'

'Your soup smells delicious,' she murmured, an odd little catch in her voice as she made an effort to dispell the fears which wouldn't leave her completely. 'Have you a magic wand as well as everything else?'

'Everything else?'

'You appear to have everything . . .'

He smiled sardonically. 'I don't have Enos yet, and

the soup is out of a packet. I had only to add water and
cook it for a few minutes.'

'May I have some?' she asked, her appetite
surprisingly restored. 'I can't think how you've
managed it.' She was startled to hear herself teasing as
he poured them both a generous helping. 'Was all this,'
she waved a hand to include the rest of what seemed a
veritable feast, 'also out of a packet.'

He nodded idly, tossing her a chunk of new bread.
'We keep emergency rations in the helicopters.
Occasionally they come in useful.'

As they ate the rest of the food, which was also
cooked expertly, Andreas looked at her consideringly. 'I
sensed you contemplating the impossibility of living
here, so have you reached a decision?'

Pushing away her half finished glass of wine, Lisa
glanced at him quickly. 'How can you know I've
come to any such conclusion?'

A dark brow rose. 'Your dejected stance maybe.'

He must have come back while she had been standing
on the cliffs to have noticed this. He must have moved like
a cat, for she hadn't heard a thing. Lifting her chin, she
said coolly. 'I'll admit I do find Enos rather daunting, but
I'm not a woman to be defeated by the first ditch.'

He inclined his head mockingly. 'If you had been,
you could scarcely have survived the gossip about you
in London.'

'Because I married an older man?'

'That, and your subsequent affairs.' He watched her
stiffening face cynically. 'Haven't you a lover pining for
you at this very moment, Mrs Fielding? Wouldn't it be
wiser to sign the agreement I have drawn up and hasten
back to his arms?'

'I have no lover anywhere!' she retorted tersely, then
regretted wasting her breath at the purring expression in
the black eyes.

'I expect you need a rest sometimes,' he remarked
outrageously.

She threw him an icy glance, hands clenching. Philip had deliberately fostered some of the gossip about her in order to combat his lady-friend's jealousy. Since then, news hungry media had filled empty spaces by speculating over her. That she wasn't alone in suffering from this modern hazard, didn't make the pain and humiliation less unbearable.

Keeping her voice steady, she ignored Andreas's gibe and changed the subject determinedly. 'There must be a jetty or landing stage somewhere?'

'There is,' he agreed suavely, 'but it's a difficult one which, like the house, through years of neglect, will have to be rebuilt. Shall I show it to you now you've finished your supper?'

'No.' She felt she could take his word for it. 'I get the general picture.'

He smiled confidently. 'And—the verdict?'

'Mr Andreas!' she spluttered. 'So far as I am concerned, there isn't one yet. You have to give me time and, as I asked you earlier, stop pushing me into doing something I may regret. Do you ever make a move yourself before you are sure of it?'

'So . . .' His eyes narrowed to hostile slits. 'You insist, madame, on dithering, though I suspect you dither deliberately. Do you know,' he barked harshly, 'I believed I knew all there was to know about women but something about you defeats me.'

'Oh!' Lisa murmured innocently, 'that must be a feather in my cap, Mr Andreas.'

'Not for long,' he mocked. 'I think I just about have you summed up. You refuse more than twice what the island is worth. In my offices, in Athens, you look fragile and helpless, on the verge of tears, yet you don't faint or go into hysterics on finding yourself alone here with me. Quite the opposite, in fact. You worry and bother over your appearance then confront me with your hair down and a glowing face.'

That was because she had reached certain conclusions. Private ones!

'And,' Andreas continued smoothly, 'it now seems quite obvious that you are more interested in me than my money.'

Lisa swallowed hard as she blazed at him. 'That is completely nonsensical, Mr Andreas!'

'Alex.'

Staring at him, her mouth slack with astonishment, she realised he would take a lot of convincing that she was totally indifferent to him. With his looks and position, probably every woman he knew must be his for the taking. She couldn't expect him to think she was the exception.

'I wouldn't wish to be as close to you as even the use of Christian names,' she muttered, hoping to correct the monstrous impression he had that she had fallen for him.

'Wouldn't you, Lisa?' He savoured her name, proving he had no such reservations. 'Never wave a red flag in front of a bull, my dear. Before I'm finished with you, if I choose, we could be so close that when we are apart you would feel my absence like the loss of a limb. An essential part of you, you can't live without.'

Her eyes widened at the images this evoked and she gazed at him in horror. 'No!' she gasped. 'Never . . .'

'Is a long time, my dear.'

He moved closer and she croaked wildly, 'You aren't g-going to . . .'

'Take you here?'

'It would be rape,' she quavered.

'Rape?' Throwing back his dark head, Andreas laughed, loud and long, arousing Lisa to fury. When she could no longer comfortably contain, it, she raised a hand propelled by it and slapped him.

Immediately she knew she had gone too far. His face with the red marks of her fingers on it, went rigid and she had only a brief warning before he grabbed her and pulled her against him. Her startled exclamation was cut off by the pressure of his mouth, hard, hot and demanding, and she had no defence against the invasion of his tongue.

Instinctively she struggled but his strength made her puny efforts appear ridiculous. She had angered him and he was using brute force to punish her. All further resistance was subdued by the heat and roughness of his embrace. He dominated her completely and when, at last, he lifted his black head to allow her to breathe and she glared with hatred at him, he merely laughed and kissed her again. He kissed her without respect, forcing her lips apart, bruising her mouth, exerting a cruelty which would have been characteristic of his pagan ancestors.

Her slender young body went limp but he continued straining her close to him, so close that she was sickened by the feeling of his hard virility against her stomach. Yet his brutal attack aroused a response in her that took her by surprise. As he plundered her mouth, though she tried to escape him, she was aware of an uprush of warmth and sensual pleasure which drove away all coherent thought.

Lisa gasped at the sudden thrill of an overwhelming sensation like nothing she had ever experienced before. She found herself clinging to him, her arms sliding around his neck, so that it came as a shock to find herself thrust so abruptly away from him that she almost lost her balance.

As she regained it, he withdrew the hand he put out to steady her. 'I didn't mean to do that,' he said thickly, 'but you provoked me.' While Lisa stared at him, her eyes widening, he added, cynically, 'Or is your obvious dismay because I didn't continue?'

'No!' she denied, horrified that he should think this. 'If I'd realised what I was inviting . . .'

'Why make a few kisses sound like a punishment worse than death?' he growled sarcastically. 'You can't be exactly allergic to them.'

She didn't miss his veiled contempt but was getting used to it. She went pale, but looked at him steadily, refusing to lower either her lashes or her pride so he might claim even a brief victory. What would he say, she wondered dispassionately, if she told him he was the first man to have kissed her in years?

'I'm going for a walk,' Andreas said, shrugging his broad shoulders when she remained silent and didn't retaliate. 'Would you care to come with me?'

'No, thank you,' she refused quickly. Her legs felt suddenly too weak to tackle the roughness of the ground he would be walking over and she suspected he would rather be alone.

'As you like,' he nodded indifferently, 'but there won't be time before we leave in the morning.'

Watching him striding away from her into the gathering dusk, Lisa's throat grew dry with shame as she recalled how she had felt in his arms. Unable to understand how her first rejection of him had changed, after being so incensed when he had first grabbed hold of her, she began clumsily disposing of the remains of their meal while trying to find an excuse for her inexplicable behaviour.

She had no wish, as Andreas had implied, to make a big thing of a few kisses but she was sure she had never responded to a man like that before. As Philip Fielding's wife, she had met men from all walks of life but never one like Alex Andreas. The tall Greek was outside her experience—with a mirthless grimace, she supposed she could be outside his. Because of the gossip he had heard, he believed she was no better than a common prostitute, while, in reality, she knew next to nothing about men. Before she was married, she had been kissed a few times but with over-protective parents and a greater interest in other things, she had never indulged, as many of her friends had, in easy promiscuity.

Philip had never touched her or shown any interest in

doing so, and she had grown fastidious. It had been easier to convince herself, when forced to lead an almost cloistered existence, that sex didn't interest her. She became aware now that she had grown a protective shell over her emotions until she no longer recognised she had any. But when Andreas had kissed her something had happened. He may have been brutal but he had certainly shattered her preconceived image of herself as someone cold and unfeeling. Though she refused to try and analyse what had happened to her in Andreas's arms, she was ready to own that after knowing him only a few hours he already represented a menacing force in her life, a force definitely threatening to its painless, if dull, tranquillity.

In future, Lisa resolved, she must do everything she could to defend herself against him. Because she had suffered so much through the press and other people's cruel remarks regarding her marriage, she was determined to guard that tranquillity at all cost. After leaving Greece, she wouldn't see Andreas again, any further negotiations with him must be conducted through Edward.

The evening grew dark and chill and long before Andreas returned, Lisa was shivering.

'Why didn't you get into one of the sleeping-bags?' he asked impatiently.

'I wasn't sure where we were to sleep,' she answered unsteadily.

If he heard her voice shaking, he ignored it. 'Under the stars, of course,' he replied derisively. 'Unless you're too pampered to even consider it?'

'I've never been pampered,' she retorted, refraining from explaining that she wasn't quite over a bad dose of 'flu. He would merely say she should have worn something warmer, which would probably lead to another quarrel.

'Well, as you haven't much choice, we won't argue over it,' he said curtly, standing over her until she got into her sleeping-bag before slipping into his own. He was very near. Lisa closed her eyes tightly so she couldn't see him but she could still hear his steady breathing. She didn't reply when he asked if she was comfortable, her throat was so choked with unaccountable tears, she couldn't trust herself to speak.

Sometime during the night she woke, finding herself very hot then suddenly shivering. Drowsily she recalled being like this when she had the 'flu. For a while she watched the stars resignedly, liking the feel of the cool wind on her burning cheeks, then she dozed again.

The next thing she knew, Andreas was shaking her, informing her it was almost six and Paul would be here any minute.

'You can wash and have breakfast at my apartment,' he said, as she struggled to her feet and made abortive attempts to tidy her tumbled hair. 'My helipad is practically on the roof.'

Lisa blinked as he smiled at her. This morning he looked and sounded almost friendly. She tried to smile in response but her face felt stiff and her legs wobbly. She managed to roll up her sleeping-bag but it was a struggle.

She remembered little of the journey back to Athens. The strange lethargy that had attacked her during the night stayed with her and, to her dismay, as they landed in the city and she got out of the helicopter everything went black. The last thing she was aware of was Andreas's startled exclamation as he caught her as she swayed.

When she came to, she was confused to discover she was in bed in a large room, with Andreas pacing the floor beside her.

'Where am I?' she asked in a hoarse whisper.

He spun around as she spoke to him, the degree of relief on his hard features surprising her. He answered her apprehensive query as if his one aim in life was to reassure her. 'In Athens, in my apartment. Don't you remember fainting when you got out of the chopper? You went out like a light, I didn't know what was the matter.'

Lisa frowned. She remembered feeling ill but she was sure she was quite all right now.

Gazing at Andreas, she tried to speak firmly. 'I think you made a mistake in imagining there was anything wrong with me. I must return to my hotel.'

'Impossible,' he overruled with equal firmness.

Sensing the steel behind the flash of white teeth which accompanied his words, Lisa was again reminded that here was a man used to exerting authority, having his every word considered law! Well, as far as she was concerned, this cut no ice! Never again would she allow herself to be taken over. With Andreas, she would have to be careful, of course. It might be wiser, until she escaped from him, not to let him know what she was thinking.

Without realising how the stubborn set of her small face gave her away, she began easing herself cautiously upright. Her indignation when Andreas dropped down beside her and pushed her firmly back against her pillows again was very apparent but he took no more notice of her angry scowl than he might have done a child.

'Hush, now,' he soothed quietly.

Suddenly, to Lisa's dismay, she burst into tears. Perhaps it was the kindness in his voice that did it but once she started crying she couldn't seem to stop. Sobs choked her throat so she couldn't even beg him to leave her alone. His big hands were too much for her, she couldn't fight them when they pulled her into his arms. Within seconds he was dabbing at her wet cheeks with a clean handkerchief he had taken from his pocket and mopping up the residue with his mouth.

'You always smell of flowers,' he purred. 'The last thing I'd ever have connected you with—flowers and tears.'

He made her sound so hard that Lisa was jerked out of the numbed stupor into which his hands and warm mouth seemed to have rendered her. Appalled, she pushed him away.

He let her go but not before planting a growling kiss on her shaking lips. 'Do not fight me, Lisa,' he warned. 'Opposition brings out the worst in me.' While Lisa gulped and tried to steady her unevenly beating heart, his eyes narrowed on her flushed face and he asked sharply, 'Were you ill before you came to Greece?'

'I had a cold,' she replied evasively.

His dark brows rose sceptically. 'Nothing more?'

'Influenza, then,' she admitted reluctantly, 'but I'd recovered.'

'Not as well as you thought,' he retorted curtly. 'You got chilled to the bone on Enos.' His eyes smouldered over her. 'Why didn't you mention you were still weak?'

'I didn't realise I was,' she replied stiffly. 'But if I did have a brief relapse, I'm sure it wasn't bad enough to justify all this!'

He didn't waste breath arguing as she gazed at him resentfully. Getting to his feet, he tossed her the robe she hadn't noticed lying on the foot of the bed. 'Put that on,' he commanded, a no nonsense note in his voice, 'and we shall soon see how well you are.'

Lisa caught the robe but didn't speak—she was too busy staring at it. 'How did this get here?' she exclaimed. 'It's mine, but it was at the hotel . . .'

'It was,' he agreed with supreme amiability, 'until I sent Paul to settle your bill and collect your things.'

'You—did what?' she stammered incredulously.

'Hush!' He made soothing motions with his hands, his face full of bland innocence. 'It was the least I could do as I am responsible for the deterioration in your condition and a hotel is no place to be ill in.'

The anger in Lisa's eyes faded a little but she still stared at him uncertainly. On the face of it, Andreas sounded as if he was merely being kind and considerate, so why did her mind positively reek with suspicion? Her relapse hadn't been that bad, but he hadn't hesitated in taking advantage of it. In bringing her here he had her at his mercy—and he wanted that paper signed!

About to accuse him of this, she paused, as she had done before. If he was trying to blind her with kindness, wouldn't it pay her to pretend she couldn't see through him? Before she signed anything she wanted to talk to Edward, but Andreas, she sensed, was determined to have things settled immediately, regardless of her wishes.

'Put on your robe,' Andreas said again, as she made no move to obey him but appeared to accept his suave explanation.

She frowned, as if only just realising what he was saying. 'I don't really need it, surely?' she protested, believing she was still dressed. Then colour rushed to her face as she glanced down at herself and saw, to her astonishment, that instead of her dress she was wearing one of her own silky nightgowns. Far from being decently covered, she had only thin blue straps over her shoulders and the almost see-through material did little to conceal the voluptuous curves of her breasts. 'Oh!' she exclaimed, snatching the sheet convulsively up to her chin. 'How did I get like this?'

'It amazes me how you can still blush,' he murmured abstractedly.

'Mr—Andreas!' she croaked, for once too disturbed in other ways to let his taunts bother her.

'Don't worry.' He smiled cynically, raising his eyes. 'The doctor and nurse I called were responsible.'

The relief Lisa felt that it hadn't been Andreas who had undressed her was short-lived. 'Doctor?' She frowned. 'What was a doctor for?'

'I sent for him,' Andreas explained, 'when I couldn't revive you after we returned from the island.'

'There was no need.'

'As it turned out, there wasn't,' he allowed. 'But I

had to be sure. When Darius was here, however, he asked me to give you a bit of advice. You are to take things easy for the next few days. You are still in delicate health.'

'If I had been, would I have survived the way you treated me yesterday?' she retorted spiritedly.

She wasn't really surprised when instead of apologising, he merely threw back his head and laughed, but she was rather startled by the comment he made.

'I don't altogether regret yesterday, Lisa. Occasionally your eyes had a sparkle in them, more in keeping with your age.'

Lisa winced and shrank away from him. He had an uncanny knack of hitting her where she was most vulnerable. He thought her lack of sparkle came from over satiated senses while it really sprang from a determination to hold herself aloof from people, so she could no longer be hurt by them. Whether, yesterday, it was Andreas or the island she had responded to, she couldn't be sure, but she had felt differently. Her only regret was that it had been obvious, as it would seem a waste of time to try and convince him he was mistaken.

Evasively she shook her head, letting her eyes darken wearily. 'You're probably right but I can't seem to remember a lot about what happened yesterday. And I feel too tired to think . . .'

Immediately he was all benign concern, betraying, she thought derisively, that he only approved of women when they were weak and helpless and giving in to him! 'Of course you are tired,' he commiserated, whilst not bothering to hide his satisfaction. 'You must rest, my dear, as the doctor ordered.'

Gently he took the robe she was still clutching from her and threw it over a chair. Lisa managed to remain submissive as he turned back to her and arranged her covers comfortably around her again.

Brushing the thick, fair hair from her face with

careful hands, he smiled into her eyes as he bent solicitously over her. 'I have to go to my office for a few hours, Lisa, and you must stay in bed until I return. Then, if you feel stronger, we shall see . . .'

See—what? Lisa watched him go, apprehensively, listening to the sounds of his departure in the hall. Andreas's deep voice mingled with a much gentler one, then there came the noise of a door closing and silence. So far, so good, she thought.

A woman came in with a tray. She must be one of Andreas's servants. Lisa imagined he would have a large staff, wherever he lived.

The woman had only a few words of English while Lisa spoke no Greek. It was strange, she frowned, how Philip had insisted she studied several languages but not Greek. Only once had she commented on this and he had grown so angry she had never mentioned it again. This, feeding as it did her growing curiosity regarding his involvement with Andreas and Enos, made her suddenly impatient. If she did learn the bare facts, and this must be all she could hope for, they might only expose some sordid little story of no real interest. What ought to be concerning her more, was getting out of here and back to London!

Pretending to be on the verge of sleep, she gave the servant a humbly grateful smile as the tray was deposited on her lap. Before the woman left, she managed to make her understand she wished to sleep all afternoon and didn't wish to be disturbed.

After she had gone, Lisa hurriedly placed the tray on the floor and using the bedside telephone, rang the airport. To her relief, there was a cancellation on a flight leaving for London in less than two hours.

Next she engaged a taxi. She knew exactly how to get one as she had used one to get from the hotel to Alex Andreas's offices. In a very few minutes she had arranged to be picked up outside. Fortunately the address of the apartment was written on a handbook which contained a list of telephone numbers. Otherwise, she would have had no idea where she was.

Half an hour later, speeding in the taxi to the airport, Lisa was amazed at the way her luck had held out. On completing her telephone calls she had dressed quickly and, with only her handbag in her hand, had simply walked out of the apartment. The staff, obviously believing she was resting quietly, were nowhere to be seen. At any rate, no one tried to stop her, but although she was triumphant at having managed to elude Andreas so easily, she couldn't help feeling worried over what he might say to the servants when he discovered she was gone.

Hours later, on arriving home, she almost had to pinch herself before she could believe she was actually there. For a while, at the airport at Ellinikon, she had felt so shaky she had wondered doubtfully if she would be able to make it, but a cup of coffee had soon restored her strength. She had felt so much better that, on the plane, she had dismissed her collapse in Athens, as partly due to apprehension. Even someone at the very peak of physical fitness might have suffered from being exposed to Andreas's overbearing tactics.

Letting herself in through her front door, she locked it again swiftly and was standing staring at it anxiously when she suddenly realised what she was doing. Drawing a deep breath, she turned away, walking resolutely into the kitchen to put on the kettle. Andreas wasn't going to be following her here, for heaven's sake! There was no need to reduce herself to a nervous wreck over something that wasn't likely to happen.

Yet as she made a cup of tea and sat drinking it, her mind continued to slip stubbornly back over the past forty-eight hours. Recalling how Andreas had persuaded her against her will to go to Enos, then taken advantage of her subsequent breakdown to imprison her in his apartment, she shuddered to think what other means he may have resorted to, in order to get possession of the island, if she hadn't managed to get away from him.

After a restless night, plagued by impossible but frightening nightmares of Andreas breaking her door down, she got up and went for a walk to try and relax. Then, after making an early breakfast, which she found she couldn't eat, she rang Edward's office and made an appointment to see him. His secretary arranged for her to see him at midday, which was the earliest time available.

The morning dragged. She couldn't settle to anything, and even when she picked up a newspaper, Andreas's dark face came between her and the printed page. Just as well, she thought, throwing the newspaper away in disgust. If she read on she might only come across some reference to him that she would rather not see. Her mind was already disturbed enough by him and she wanted it clear so she could present her case intelligently to Edward.

She arrived at his office a few minutes early but he was ready for her.

'Lisa!' he exclaimed, as his secretary showed her in and closed the door. 'I didn't expect to see you today.' Rising, he ushered her to a chair, his silver head bending over her solicitously. 'I was surprised, I admit, when Jane told me you had asked for an appointment. You said you would be in Athens for at least a week.'

'I might have been—I should have liked to have been!' Lisa added with emphasis as she waited for Edward to sit down again.

'But?' he prompted, his keen grey eyes returning to her face.

Perhaps because Edward was a true friend, one of the few she had, she always found him easy to talk to. Within seconds she was relating the regrettable story of her trip to Athens, her unsatisfactory encounter with Andreas, leaving only certain bits out.

'He appears to want the island desperately,' she said. 'You'll get a shock when you hear the price he's offering.' As she revealed it, if Edward didn't exactly get a shock, his brows certainly rose. 'But he won't tell me why?'

'Why?'

'Well, there has to be a reason surely?' Lisa exclaimed, as Edward frowned. 'I mean, no one offers that kind of money, practically a small fortune, for a useless piece of land!'

Edward considered her flushed cheeks thoughtfully before he spoke. 'I assure you, my dear, the island is just that, so I hope you don't think I've been lying to you about it. It has no oil, no tourist potential and very little beauty although once, I believe, it looked a lot better than it does now.'

Lisa trusted Edward, she always had done, but this didn't stop her from feeling puzzled. 'Then why is he offering so much?'

The man before her shrugged then rubbed his chin reflectively on his clasped hands. 'If I were you, Lisa, I'd simply take what he offers and be thankful. Let Andreas worry as to what kind of a bargain he's getting.'

'If I do decide to let him have it,' she retorted firmly, 'I won't take more than what it is worth.'

'It seems to me,' Edward murmured, meeting her determined eyes blandly, after a small hesitation, 'that you have other reservations, Lisa, apart from the price?'

CHAPTER THREE

LISA's soft lips twisted. Were lawyers always as astute? 'Well, I think I'm entitled to know a little.'

'Ah . . .!' Edward's softly drawn out exclamation irritated, as did the accompanying words. 'What you are suffering from,' he twinkled, 'is known as feminine curiosity.'

Lisa laughed but sobered quickly. 'You could be right but it isn't only that. It was the way he went about it.'

'I told you, you needed me with you.'

Blindly she shook her head. 'He insulted me, Edward. Oh,' she exclaimed bitterly, 'I know I should be used to being insulted by now . . .'

'And getting over it,' he injected gently, his eyes focused worriedly on her white face.

Numbly she stared at him. 'That's the trouble, I'm not. Andreas must have had someone collect all the evidence against me they could lay hands on. He seemed to think . . .' she couldn't bear to confess he had actually said it, 'I'm no better than a common prostitute, willing to sell my soul as well as my body for money.'

'Good lord!' Even Edward went pale as he jumped up to pat her shoulder consolingly. 'We both know you are completely innocent, but you have to understand a lot of people have no means of checking what they read or hear.'

'Yet they're so willing to believe.' Her eyes darkened with pain. 'He didn't even give me the benefit of the doubt.'

Edward frowned, smothering his anger. 'I'd have thought he would have been more diplomatic.'

41

'Most people in his position would have been,' she agreed bleakly, 'but Mr Andreas is obviously a law unto himself.'

Edward nodded. 'I'm afraid circumstances have made him like that, Lisa. He's not wholly to blame. He has so much power there must be few situations he can't control exactly as he wishes.'

This merely made her feel more obstinate. Andreas might dominate those who worked for him and influence others but he had no such jurisdiction over her! She must make this plain.

'I realise,' she said drily, 'that Mr Andreas is used to manipulating people, but you must write and tell him that Enos will only be sold at the price I stipulate and I will only sell to him if he is prepared to answer a few questions.'

'He is in London now.' Edward's mouth curved in what suspiciously resembled grim amusement.

'Now?' Lisa felt strangely shattered. 'Not because of Enos, surely?'

'That I can't say,' Edward shrugged, 'but I do know my telephone has been red hot all morning. He wishes to see you and demands your address.'

Lisa shivered again, this time with very real alarm. 'You—didn't give it to him?'

He smiled thinly. 'I'm not that injudicious, my dear.'

'Why should I see him?' Lisa's eyes blazed as her thoughts went off at a tangent. 'He disapproves of me and disliked Philip. If I agreed to meet him it would just be to listen to more insults.'

'He knew Philip.' Edward frowned. 'I don't know a great deal more about their acquaintance than you do but I feel there is some bitterness somewhere, possibly quite unconnected with you. Have you tried talking to Andreas about your marriage? He might be surprised to learn that, contrary to what he appears to believe, Philip's fortune was frittered away on another woman.'

'Andreas is a stranger, Edward,' Lisa reminded him

sharply, wondering that she should have to. 'I couldn't discuss my marriage with him. Besides, if I did, I would have to name names, and I have neither inclination nor proof. Knowing Gilda, I could even find myself in a lawsuit, charged with defamation of character. No!' she exclaimed, jumping to her feet. 'Mr Andreas and I have nothing more to say to each other. Inform him, Edward, if he rings again, that I need more time, anything you like, but I don't wish to see him again.'

'You won't—and I can't, put him off indefinitely, my dear.'

'I know,' she realised, feeling terribly threatened. 'I don't expect you to work miracles or to put your livelihood at risk, but I won't be bullied!'

'And—your address?'

Lisa gazed at Edward anxiously. 'I suppose he could get it,' she fretted. 'For all the good it might do him, you can give it to him. But if you do,' she added shortly, 'you may also mention that I won't be pestered. Contrary to what Mr Andreas thinks, I am not trying to attract him by being awkward.'

Lisa didn't return to Fulham straight away after leaving Edward. If Andreas intended beating a path to her door, she might be wiser not to be in for a while. She had anticipated he would be furious over her hasty departure from Greece, without anything being settled between them, but she hadn't expected he would follow her to England. He might be combining a lightning visit to London with other business but because she was certain he'd had no immediate intention of leaving Athens while she had been there, she guessed Enos must be uppermost in his mind.

When she judged Andreas would be having lunch, she slipped back home, angry that she should be feeling like a fugitive. After making herself some coffee, she had a shower and slept afterwards, blaming her continuing tiredness on the distinctly disturbing session she'd had with Edward.

She awoke with a scream on her lips, from a bad dream in which Andreas was pursuing her. The fading light told her it was growing late and someone was pounding on her door.

Still wearing the robe she had put on after her shower, she merely paused long enough to pull herself together and wipe the perspiration from her face before going to answer it.

Because of her bad dream, her mind wasn't functioning properly. She hadn't thought beyond a neighbour who sometimes popped in and could have wept at her own stupidity on opening the door and finding Andreas standing on the step. How could she have forgotten him!

He pushed past her and was inside, before she could stop him, dropping a flight bag, which she recognised as her own at her feet. 'Good-evening, Lisa, I've brought your clothes,' he began with cool formality, then paused. 'There's something wrong?' he asked, his black gaze focusing sharply on her damp cheeks.

'Nothing I can't put right if you'll just go,' she returned with equal sharpness. 'You have a nerve coming here!'

'Lisa!'

'Oh, all right.' She gave in weakly. Perhaps she was being unreasonable. 'I fell asleep and was having a bad dream.'

'What about?' Putting her firmly aside, he closed the door behind him.

If she had been more composed she might have made a joke of it and told him, but with tears still trickling inexplicably down her cheeks, she couldn't give him the satisfaction of knowing he could upset her.

'Why did you come here?' she countered, scrubbing helplessly at her tears with her fists.

Wryly he handed her his handkerchief. 'Why did you run away?'

Was that the answer? 'Not so you would come

running after me,' she replied tautly, drying her face with his handkerchief and thinking she was making a habit of it.

'You must have known I would.' The concern in his eyes was replaced by cynical observation. 'It's been clear to me since we met that you know all the little tricks.'

'Mr Andreas!' she retorted, immediately rattled. 'I saw my solicitor, this morning, and if you have anything more to say to me, you must get in touch with him. He,' she finished grandly, 'is fully conversant with my wishes.'

'Lisa,' he growled, dark eyes smouldering briefly, 'stop prevaricating. We both know that Edward Sterne can't break the deadlock between us. Only you can do that.'

'But this doesn't give you the right to persecute me.'

He said something harsh in Greek then suddenly, to her amazement, smiled and asked, 'Have you dined yet?'

'No,' she replied blankly, 'I told you, I've been asleep.'

'Recovered from your fever, have you?'

Lisa nodded uncertainly.

'Then have dinner with me?'

'I might have other plans,' she said, startled at his audacity.

'I don't doubt it.' Again a cynical expression flickered through his eyes. 'But whatever arrangements you have made, you can cancel them.'

Such arrogance! She stared at him for a moment in patent disbelief, trying to find a retort deflating enough to quell him, but before she could he took the wind from her sails by putting a hand out and stroking it gently over her tousled hair and suggesting mildly. 'Why not run upstairs and get dressed and stop arguing?'

If she didn't, how was she to get rid of him? It

suddenly occurred to her that he could remain here for hours if she didn't agree. Remembering the kind of persuasion he had used in Athens when she had defied him, she felt her nerves tighten apprehensively. 'Oh, very well,' she consented mutinously.

Abruptly he let go of her. 'Your enthusiasm is scarcely flattering,' he murmured ironically. 'However, I don't think you will similarly disappoint me with your appearance.'

Running upstairs, Lisa couldn't be as sure. She had only been out once, in the evening, since Philip had died and that had proved an experience she had no wish to repeat.

To distract her thoughts from that evening, she quickly rinsed and dried her face then opened her wardrobe door. To an idle observer, it would seem she had a fantastic collection of clothes. It was all there, something to suit every possible occasion—evening dresses, daywear, both casual and practical, feminine and elegant. There were trouser suits, jacket and skirt suits, short dresses, long ones, soft blouses, shoes, scarfs, handbags, every possible accessory. Philip had insisted she had everything, he'd demanded she be impeccably gowned and made-up whenever he took her out or she entertained for him.

Her evening clothes were brilliant. Philip had liked certain colours on certain days, he had never been able to abide blue on Mondays, so her wardrobe of long dresses resembled a rainbow, many as yet unworn. Lisa's eyes raced over the silks and satins, the velvet tunics and long sleek skirts. Philip had only seen her as a possession, there for the purpose of impressing, and like all his possessions she'd had to be perfect.

Her eyes settled on a silky sheath in red. Why not? Lisa's mind raced ahead. Andreas thought of her as a scarlet woman. In his country, a woman who lost her husband might wear black for the rest of her life. Why not shock him? He expected to be shocked so why disappoint him?

The germ of bitter mischief grew in Lisa's mind until she found herself grasping the red dress and zipping herself into it. It curved over her hips and breasts like a second skin, exposing most of the latter to the discerning eye through layers of gauzy material.

Swiftly ignoring a niggle of doubt, she searched for the appropriate make-up and began painting her face. Then, after brushing her hair and throwing off the protective towel she had thrown over her shoulders, she coiled the thick, gleaming strands on top of her head in a sophisticated arrangement. Next came spiky heeled gold sandals, a gold evening bag and her mink cape. Andreas could wait until later for the full unveiling. A tiny smile of pure malice curved Lisa's soft lips as she envisaged his face. If he thought of her as a call girl now, what would his opinion be of her then?

Before her courage failed her, she ran back downstairs. He was in the lounge, to which she had directed him after he had refused anything to drink. She suddenly realised he was in evening dress himself and her mind darkened with suspicion. He must have been very confident that she would agree to go out with him!

He swung around as he heard her in the doorway, an expression in his black eyes she couldn't define. They smouldered and gleamed all over her, a certain something in their depth which looked like hunger. Hunger or desire? She couldn't be sure, but whatever it was it drew from her an unwelcome response. She felt her heartbeats quicken and a peculiar warmth rising unaccountably in her breast.

Again came the touch of his fingers, as he swiftly closed the distance between them. They raised her chin, so he could see her face clearly. 'You're beautiful,' he said thickly, 'whatever else you may be.'

What did he mean? Fool—did she have to wonder! Answering her own question caustically, Lisa jerked away from him and asked coolly, 'Are your compliments always double-edged, Mr Andreas?'

He smiled mockingly. 'You must allow for a little human scepticism, Lisa, and the name's Alex. I don't wish to have to tell you again.'

Would she ever be able to manage it? Lisa gazed at him doubtfully until her empty stomach reminded her she had scarcely eaten all day. 'You promised me dinner,' she murmured somewhat irrelevantly.

'So I did,' he agreed, turning her towards the door. 'I regret not suggesting we dined here . . .'

Did he indeed! Well, she wasn't ready for that kind of intimacy yet, if ever she would be, with him! Pretending to be deaf to the invitation in his voice, she made no reply.

With a sigh, he secured the door behind her and handed her into his expensive car. It gleamed, black and silver, reflecting the appearance and affluence of its owner. Lisa shivered as he got in beside her.

'Where are your servants?' he asked, glancing at her with a slight frown as he shot off down the street.

'I don't have any.'

'You—live alone?'

'Yes.' Sensing his disapproval, she kept her answers brief.

This didn't deter him and she was drily amused that some aspects of her life appeared to puzzle him. 'This is rather a poor area, is it not? Why do you choose to live here when you could afford something better?'

'How do you know what I can afford?' she retorted sharply.

He flicked her a sardonic glance. 'Surely, with what Philip left you . . .?'

'He didn't leave me that much,' she snapped, tiring of his derisive curiosity.

'Perhaps he thought you wouldn't be long in finding another—protector?'

Having no wish to defend the virtue Andreas was

determined to believe she didn't have, and frightened she might say too much if she allowed herself to reply, Lisa bit her lip and sat in angry silence until he drew up outside a famous and popular establishment in the West End.

Within seconds of the car being driven away by an attendant they were walking towards the marble steps leading to the canopied portico. It all happened so quickly that Lisa hadn't time to protest that she would rather have gone somewhere less ostentatious. Her worst fears were realised, though, when cameras began flashing and she recognised behind them one or two familiar faces.

Apprehensively she shrank against Andreas who, automatically, put an arm protectively around her. This made her cringe all the more as she realised he had mistaken her reaction and, unlike her, was enjoying and even encouraging the publicity.

'I didn't expect to be subject to this!' she murmured despairingly.

'How well do you know Mrs Fielding, Mr Andreas?' a Fleet Street gossip columnist called impudently.

Andreas merely grinned as he pulled a shocked Lisa into his arms and kissed her thoroughly.

As his hard lips bruised hers, she was electrically aware of him in every bone of her body while the laughing witticisms of the reporters blurred in her pounding ears. Andreas had taken her by surprise and, in an instant, rendered her so helpless that she couldn't find the strength to detach herself from his amused arms. He was enjoying himself, ran her dazed, incredulous thoughts, otherwise he wouldn't be putting on a performance like this, helping to fill the fictitious corners of the dailies. Mostly men like Andreas ignored the press, refusing to be interviewed and giving only brusque replies when cornered, but, occasionally they appeared to delight in doing an about turn and really giving them something to write about.

Andreas's assault on her lips seemed to last an eternity but in reality it was very brief. Nevertheless, by the time he released her she was shaking.

His eyes narrowed on her sheet-white face impatiently but he didn't apologise as he swept her inside. 'You didn't expect to be taken somewhere quiet in that dress, did you?' he taunted softly.

Mortification put colour back into Lisa's cheeks and stiffened her wavering senses. 'I didn't expect to be mauled in public!'

Andreas snapped, 'I let you off lightly and you know it. I should have thought someone like you could have taken a joke like that in your stride.'

'You make me sound notorious!' she muttered angrily, as they sat down at the table to which the headwaiter had conducted them deferentially after she had disposed of her cape.

Andreas's mouth twisted as he ordered two drinks then waved the menus away until later. 'You aren't accusing me of ruining your reputation, are you? That happened long before we met. Remember, I know all about you.'

'No you don't,' she blazed, 'but that's not important.'

'I agree,' he deliberately misconstrued. 'It never pays to be too retrospective.' Lifting his glass of wine as it arrived, he proposed suavely, 'Here's to us and the coming months. I promise, if you play your cards right and stop being stubborn, you will find them extremely rewarding.'

Lisa left her own wine severely alone, otherwise she might have thrown it over him. Never before had she met a man with such supreme confidence. She hated the almost proprietorial expression in his eyes as they insolently studied her and came to rest on the revealing bodice of her dress.

Again she regretted wearing it but she wasn't going to be ashamed of either it or herself! 'Mr Andreas—Alex,' she amended stiffly as his face darkened, 'we have a little business to discuss, if you won't negotiate with Edward, but that is all. And that is all there is going to be between us! You want Enos but you don't have to pretend you want me as well.'

His dark brows lowered. 'Once I have the island, you don't imagine that will be the end of it, do you? It will only be the beginning.'

Lisa stared at him in exasperation even while her heart was thudding at something oddly threatening in his voice. 'I suspect you are trying to flatter me, in a roundabout way,' she replied uncertainly. 'But I can assure you it isn't necessary. I have decided to let you have the island, providing you don't insist on paying me an inflated price. I might have told you in Greece if you hadn't scared me into running away . . .'

'Never do that again,' he warned darkly. 'Let me tell you, Lisa, if I hadn't arrived at the airport five minutes too late, I would have dragged you off that plane.'

'Five minutes . . .' Her eyes widened apprehensively.

'Yes,' he grated. 'The servants must have checked almost as soon as you closed the apartment door. Naturally they rang my office but the message didn't reach me immediately. I should have telephoned the airport and had them stop you instead of believing I had time to do it myself.'

'How would that have helped you?' she scorned.

His mouth tightened. 'You wouldn't have got that far again until everything had been settled.'

'Well, I'm selling you the island now,' she retorted. 'So after this evening we don't have to see each other again.'

'Ha!' he laughed. 'You don't really believe that?'

She didn't reply. Let him think what he liked! If he persisted in seeing her, she could easily disappear for a few days until he tired of looking for her.

'I should like to know one thing,' she said, after a brief pause. 'How Philip came by Enos in the first place. I know I've asked you before and you've declined to answer, but I don't think I'm being unreasonable.'

'Are you making this a condition?'

'No.' She shook her head. 'I'm curious but I'm not bargaining.'

He contemplated his glass with a sigh. 'If Enos only concerned me I might tell you, but it doesn't.'

She laughed ruefully. 'You're only making me feel worse.'

'Possibly,' he allowed with a slight smile. 'The best I can do about Enos is to advise you to forget it.'

She supposed he was right but it wasn't easy for she was sure that the island's seemingly eventful history should tell her something. Did he intend restoring the island and living there himself, or with someone else, as he had mentioned another person?

Attempting to dismiss such thoughts from her mind, she asked another, vaguely related, question. 'Where do you live, Alex, while you are in London?'

His watchful glance relaxed slightly. 'I have a penthouse.'

'Soulless places.'

'I don't exactly love them, either,' he commented drily. 'They are merely a convenience I would find difficult to do without. My real home is in Greece.'

'Athens?'

'No. An island.'

'An—island?' Her eyes widened in surprise, despite her resolve to express only a casual interest in his affairs. 'If you already have an island, why do you want Enos so badly?'

'Back to square one?' he murmured, a smile of amusement touching his mouth.

She flushed and said tartly, 'Sorry I asked.'

If something about her deliberate flippancy annoyed him, he disguised it quickly. 'The island where I make my home is nothing like Enos.'

'You live there alone?'

'Most of the time.'

Which didn't tell her much. It was a swift and bland admission from which, she guessed shrewdly, he left her to draw her own conclusions. While he was there he probably entertained a woman friend. She had seen these mentioned in the press he disdained to let worry him. A man like Andreas, rich, good-looking and still in his thirties, would know a lot of women and she couldn't understand why the idea was suddenly repugnant to her.

'Were you born there?' she asked hastily.

'No,' he replied patiently. 'I haven't had it all that long but I've grown fond of it.'

Lisa could tell he had by the way his face softened. 'You must want to hurry back to it,' she said hopefully.

His eyes glinted, swiftly seeing through her attempted strategy. 'I intend staying in London for the next few weeks, at least. Haven't I already told you, Lisa, you won't get rid of me so easily?'

The arrival of their waiters with the menu again provided a welcome interruption. Lisa nodded inattentively as Andreas suggested various dishes. She couldn't believe he was serious about remaining in London. More likely it would be business which kept him here and he was merely enjoying himself in pretending it was because of her.

The food was wonderful when it arrived, yet though she was still hungry, her appetite was soon satisfied and she finished up with half of her dinner left on her plate.

'You should eat more,' Alex growled, toasting her with the champagne which accompanied the sweet. 'You are too thin.' His eyes wandered to her breasts, which tightened alarmingly beneath his prolonged scrutiny. 'It surprises me that you aren't thin all over. I wonder . . .'

What he wondered, insinuatingly, was all too plain! Lisa glared at him angrily. 'You have a mind like a cesspool!' she exploded, going hot all over.

'Just because I make a remark you don't like?'

'A remark like that only comes under one category.'

His mouth quirked in an amused grin. 'I like you when your eyes are flashing. It does away with the frozen image you're fond of projecting and makes me want,' he paused fractionally, 'to get to know you better.'

That will be the day! she thought morosely. 'I don't think you are interested in women enough to want to really get to know them, Alex,' she retorted tartly. 'You meet one who attracts you but all you really see is her body.'

'What's wrong with that?' he growled, his amusement fading.

'Nothing,' she shrugged, 'providing the lady is only interested in one thing too.'

'And you aren't?' he jeered. 'I suppose the relevant rewards wouldn't be an incentive? I'm very good to those who please me, Lisa, as I hope you are going to find out, but I respect a woman more if she doesn't try to turn a mutually satisfying relationship into something she considers more meaningful.'

He meant love, of course, which he clearly wouldn't believe in. As for his other audacious observations, she certainly wouldn't be around to try and please him! Wishing she was more adept at cutting retorts, she was frustrated that the one she made sounded as if she was speaking from personal experience.

'Affairs of that kind can become boring, which is possibly why women look for something else.'

He stared at her as he digested what she was saying and applied his own interpretation to it. 'Philip Fielding wasn't a man I admired, as you've probably gathered. When I heard he had married, I even felt sorry for you, despite the fact that you were obviously out for all you could get. Now I wonder, with a faithless wife, who was most to be pitied?'

Lisa clamped down on her temper. Goading him wasn't doing her much good. His tongue was sharper than hers and a thousand times more cruel. 'I won't discuss my marriage.'

His contemptuous expression dissolved in a smile, like that of a big cat. 'You don't have to, Lisa, nor do we have to quarrel. You are beautiful and, more than that, your body is a living temptation to any hot-blooded male—which I certainly am. It's not difficult to imagine other men wanting you. I do, myself, and mean to have you, but let that suffice. You don't have to pretend, with me, to be anything other than yourself.'

But he wouldn't believe her when she tried to be! Lisa sighed inwardly as they left the restaurant, again attempting to dismiss the outrageous things Andreas said from her mind. Because of her marriage and the subsequent untrue gossip about her, he had her marked as a scarlet woman—matching her dress.

As she made the ironic comparison and glanced down at it wryly, she didn't see the man with the camera until it was too late and the flash nearly blinded her as she looked up. 'Oh!' she cried, again shrinking against Alex. 'Please stop them!' she choked, her voice wild.

Glancing swiftly at her hysterical face, he moved fast. A curt word from him had the photographer lowering his camera and with a swiftness that seemed incredible, he thrust Lisa into the waiting car and drove away.

'Why let them bother you?' he asked, as he had done before, with unconcealed impatience. 'You're trembling.' He placed a hand over hers to confirm it. 'They can't really do much harm.'

He believed that because he was impregnable! For a moment Lisa envied him the arrogance that enabled him to be so indifferent. 'They've never done me much good!' she muttered, removing her hand from under his.

'Look at it this way, Lisa,' he retorted coolly. 'You invited the interest of the press by marrying a much older man, and by your affairs with other men. You may regret your behaviour but take, for instance, this evening, the way you're dressed, flaunting your charms so that every man in that restaurant was staring at you openly—this doesn't indicate a change of heart. You may be trying to re-educate your mind but your sensuous nature still defies you.'

'Alex!' she flared angrily. 'I agree I've had an unfortunate past but none of it was exactly my fault. There are things I can't talk about but I can assure you I'm not what you think I am. Philip wasn't an easy man to live with, or maybe I was too young ... He didn't want me ...'

'And he objected when other men did.'

'No!' she insisted. 'You have it all wrong.'

He shrugged but seemed disinclined to continue the conversation and suddenly Lisa wearied of it herself. They drove in silence the rest of the way to Lisa's house. As he drew up outside it, she renewed her resolve to wish him a cool good night and never see him again.

She could have screamed when he was too quick for her. On her doorstep, she was so busy rehearsing a concise farewell that he took her by surprise when he reached for her bag and removed the key. Inserting it in the lock, he thrust her inside as the door swung open and he locked it behind them.

She should have remembered how he had forced his way in earlier and been prepared, but he had acted so swiftly, she hadn't had a chance. 'You have to leave!' she gasped. 'At once.'

'Lisa,' he smiled complacently, still keeping a hold of her, 'you've been ill, on your own for too long, you need company.'

What was he trying to insinuate? Lisa shook her head blindly, wishing she wasn't too tired to think clearly. She tried to throw off his detaining arm, her one objective to be rid of him. While dimly grasping the meaning behind his suave words, she felt too numb to take much notice. If he thought she went through men like a sweet addict through a pound of chocolates, well let him! It might even be fun, some unamused part of her suggested again, to encourage his bad opinion of her?'

'If I feel frustrated, in need of company,' she smiled, 'I have only to pick up the telephone.'

'You little tease!' he ground out, picking her up before she could grasp what he was doing and striding with her into the lounge. As she tried to recover her breath, she caught a frightening glimpse of his face and realised her impulsive utterance had disgusted him. Instead of sending him away as she had hoped it would, it had merely aroused something dangerous in him, making him furious.

'Let me go you—you savage,' she gulped, too overwrought to be diplomatic.

'You won't be surprised if I act like one then,' he said roughly, throwing her carelessly on to the huge sofa by the fire and coming down almost on top of her.

'Please!' she protested wildly, but further words were smothered by the predatory mouth that swooped and fastened on her trembling one, in a relentless, bruising imitation of a kiss.

The pressure he exerted was cruel in its intensity, bringing pain to her throat and the inner surfaces of her mouth as he crushed her teeth against them ruthlessly. He didn't spare her. She could feel the affront of her foolishly reckless remark turning every hard muscle of his body into steel-like cords bent on hurting. If he meant to subdue and punish, he was succeeding. Though Lisa kept her mouth shut she was terrifyingly conscious of being completely at his mercy. His strength was overwhelming and she had never been subject to a man's strength in this way before. His weight crushed her, his head blotted out the light, and though she writhed and twisted beneath him, his thighs pinioned her legs until she was completely helpless.

Briefly he raised his head, his eyes blazing with a primitive male need. 'Lisa!' he exclaimed. 'What the

devil is the matter with you? If you believe that acting
like an outraged virgin is impressing me, I'd advise you
to think again.'

'I think I hate you!' she cried.

'You don't hate me, Lisa. You don't hate what I'm
doing to you either.' Deliberately he ran his lips from
her mouth down the slim line of her neck to the pulse
that raced in her throat. 'You've become too used to
men who treat you with kid gloves all the time, weak
characters, like your late husband. You won't find me
as easy to fob off but I can teach you a lot. How to
recognise a real man, for one thing.'

CHAPTER FOUR

His cool assumption tightened Lisa's nerves and in the white-hot heat of the moment, as her angry blue eyes met his, her heart leapt in panic at what she read there.

'You won't impress me by hurting me,' she retorted.

'Lisa,' he growled, easing the wrap from her shoulders and dropping it on the floor. 'I don't intend hurting you, I never did. Wanting a woman doesn't mean being cruel to her.'

'What else would you call forcing yourself on me?'

'I'm not forcing myself on you,' he replied softly. 'There's a world of difference between that and a little gentle persuasion. And you have to see things from my point of view too, you know. You're very beautiful but something about you tempts me until I'm tormented by feelings I can scarcely control.'

His weight rested heavily on her and she felt so impotent that tears choked her throat until she could scarcely breathe. What he was saying didn't make sense but then was there anything sensible about the position she was in?

He was holding her so tightly she could feel the dark hair of his chest prickling her tender skin through the thin silk of his shirt. His heart was pounding against hers and she felt she was being taken over by some magnetic force against which her puny resistance had no effect whatsoever. Briefly this filled her with a sense of wonder and as he gazed down on her face, she could only shake her head at him in dazed confusion.

She was mesmerised by what he said for it struck an answering chord in her, but as he began kissing her again, nibbling at her lips, sliding his tongue against hers and the beating of his heart accelerated, she knew a

59

stab of cold fear. He wanted her, she suddenly realised
how much, and if he decided to take what he wanted,
would she be able to say no?

Though her senses reeled, the increasing pressure of
his hard body frightened her and she began to struggle
frantically, pushing against his chest, wrenching her
mouth free.

'Stop it,' he muttered thickly, 'I'm not hurting you
now.'

He wasn't, and a sudden awareness of this caused her
unaccountably to relax. Her agitated hands stilled as, in
a moment of weakness, she allowed herself to be
persuaded he meant her no harm. Her fears calmed
though the blood still pounded in her ears, and after a
brief hesitation she even started tentatively to return the
growing insistence of his kisses.

A small wave of pleasure washed through her which,
fanned by his mounting passion, threatened to become
a storm. His kisses had all the fire and strength of the
elements and she began to respond feverishly to him,
quite unconscious of a barrier in herself being
approached and surmounted. It wasn't until the heat of
her blood leapt to meet his and his command of himself
slipped, that she dizzily realised what her apparent
surrender was inviting.

As his mouth became wildly rampant, a thrill of
alarm shot through her which increased as he dragged
her dress from her shoulders so he could assault the
enticing curves of her breasts with his plundering lips.
Her thin cry of protest was ignored as his hands
followed the path of his lips to brush the pink tips then
stroked the flatness of her stomach and the curve of her
hips.

He didn't seem to hear the strangled whimpers
issuing from her throat but continued pressing urgent
kisses on her quivering flesh until, once more, her body
was shaking with helpless response. She might have
been lost in the flood of liquid fire beginning to devour

her, if a sudden impatience hadn't driven him into treating her as he might have done the experienced woman he obviously considered her.

As the last remnants of his restraint fled and the depth and dangers of his passion became more apparent, Lisa stiffened. Locked up inside her was a volume of answering passion and need that she daren't release because she was afraid of its power, and besides, she reminded herself, Alex was a stranger, she scarcely knew him! Again she began to struggle and knew a surge of relief when at last she seemed to get through to him. Her victory might have resulted in a snarl of frustration but he was forced to stop kissing her in order to capture her flailing hands.

'Please,' she faltered, 'I'm sorry . . .'

'What for? Leading me on then changing your mind?'

His cheekbones were flushed, his eyes glittering and stormy, filling her with shock, and though he paused she could see he had no intention of letting her go. Swiftly, as she went limp with dismay, his mouth returned to hers, intent on taking what he was obviously beginning to think of as his.

'Please, Alex,' she reiterated distractedly. 'Don't do this.'

'Lisa, for God's sake!' he gasped hoarsely, his glance ferocious on her burning face. 'You can't say no now.'

'I have to,' she replied incoherently, as his knee forced her thighs apart and she saw in his face an agonised spasm of desire.

The agony spread to his eyes and his mouth twisted but slowly his body slumped and he slackened his hold on her. She sensed he might not have won the battle he fought with himself if he hadn't noticed the fear and tears in her eyes, the sight of which appeared to affect him oddly. As if he realised the panic behind them and felt her slight body shaking beneath his, he groaned and his muscles clenched, but he stopped glaring at her.

As he subsided against her, Lisa was aware of a flood

of gratitude replacing the apprehension which had taken such a grip on her. At the mercy of an inexplicible wave of tenderness, she lifted a hand to touch him compassionately. For all her innocence, she wasn't so ignorant as to be totally unaware of the effort it must have cost him to stop when he did.

'Alex . . .' she began, but this time he wasn't listening. Her breath caught sharply as he abruptly pushed himself off her and stood up and she saw his face. He had paled and his mouth, which only minutes ago had kissed her so warmly, was a cold, tight line.

'Cover yourself,' he commanded curtly, and while she fumbled to straighten her dress, he reached for the jacket he had dispensed with. 'I'm sorry, Lisa,' he said wearily. 'You are right in your objections. I'm not given to indiscriminate sex. For the first time in my life I didn't consider the risk I was taking and take proper precautions.' He started, as if it had only just occurred to him and stared at her narrowly. 'Was that why you got in such a panic?'

'No.' Her damp cheeks flooded with colour as she shook her head.

'Then I don't understand . . .?' His puzzled expression changed to a frown which in turn changed to dawning comprehension. 'I frightened you, didn't I? Although it wasn't my fault. It's the brutality of the men you have known before who have filled you with fear. I can promise you, Lisa, it won't be like that with me.'

She stared at him in alarm. 'Alex . . .'

He smiled, his mouth relaxing, mistakenly thinking she was about to apologise for disappointing him. 'I'll give you a little time, but I won't be put off for ever, Lisa, you know that.'

'Alex, please listen!' she entreated but he shook his head quickly.

'I intend teaching you a lot of things.' He smiled. 'All the pleasures your other escorts have selfishly deprived you of.'

'I haven't been deprived of anything,' she protested wildly.

His brows merely lifted disbelievingly as he pulled her up beside him and retorted less patiently, 'No woman who has ever enjoyed belonging to a man would have been able to reject me as you have done tonight. Though you may not realise it, you have a lot to learn, things which no one has taken either the time or trouble to teach you.'

'You're wrong!' she reiterated, suddenly feeling it might save a lot of trouble if she told him the simple truth. But again, he wouldn't listen.

'No, I'm not.' Arrogantly he imposed his will over hers. 'I can recognise fear when I see it and I'm no callow youth that I can't judge the cause of it. I'm going to rid you of it, Lisa, if it's the last thing I do, but don't worry,' he added softly, as she blanched, 'for us, it will only be the beginning.'

Lisa was numbly aware of a gently proprietorial kiss pressed on her lips and the outer door closing. Automatically she obeyed Andreas's last command and locked it after him. She listened to his fading footsteps, the noise of his car starting, and stood staring at the door, a shocked expression on her face until she heard him drive away. Then, with an inarticulate little cry, she rushed upstairs to bed.

The sunshine, the next morning, coming through her window aroused her and, after wearily rubbing her drowsy eyes, she lay watching it unhappily. She had slept badly, forever dreaming of Alex Andreas and unable to get rid of his image even now she was awake. Her heart beat unevenly as she recalled the things he had said. He couldn't mean the half of what he had threatened, she was sure he had only been amusing himself while they squabbled over the price of the island. Now that that was settled, she didn't really believe she would see him again.

Lisa frowned as she sat up abruptly in bed. Forgetting

about the sunshine, she stared blindly into space. She had to admit she wasn't quite sure how she would feel if she wasn't to see him again. She brushed the hair from her suddenly hot face impatiently. It was ridiculous to feel trapped by a confusion of emotions over a man she scarcely knew. She told herself firmly she wasn't so much attracted by him as repelled, and, if she wasn't completely sure of her own feelings, at least she could be sure of his.

Alex declared he wished to get to know her better but she imagined his inclinations would soon change if she could manage to convince him she was sexually innocent. The only virgin he would wish to know would be the one he might one day marry! If she could persuade him that she would be quite unable to satisfy a man of his experience, at least it might make him leave her alone and save her the bother of having to flee from London.

The problem would be trying to prove she was telling the truth without revealing too much of her past. Even mentioning the past, however briefly, aroused such a degree of disquiet inside her as to make her wonder if a full discussion of it mightn't affect her sanity. Only Edward and Philip's lady-love, besides herself, knew the true facts of her marriage, though she doubted that Gilda Grant knew the whole of them. Gilda had certainly known that Philip had married Lisa in order to deceive her husband into believing that with a beautiful young wife, Philip Fielding would be unlikely to look at anyone else! Lisa had been shamelessly used to cloak Gilda and Philip's scandalous behaviour and it still made Lisa bitter that she had been forced into the role of an accomplice for the sake of her parents.

As clearly as if it was yesterday, she remembered how her father's boss had called her into his office and outlined what he would do for her invalid mother, should Lisa marry him. As far as her parents were concerned, Philip had kept his word, but even the best medical treatment in the world hadn't been able to save her mother and her father had died of a broken heart.

The only thing she could say in Philip's favour was that right from the beginning he had never deceived her. He had wanted to marry someone who resembled his mistress so that when other people caught a glimpse of her abroad with him, they would think it was his wife. Gilda, apparently, was too fond of the title her crippled husband provided her with to get a divorce, and there was also the drawback of her religion.

Only Philip, with his love of the dramatic and insatiable desire for excitement might have devised such a scheme, and got away with it. But for her parents, Lisa wouldn't have had anything to do with him!

To promote the glittering image which fooled everyone into thinking he was a besotted husband, Philip had sent her to an exclusive finishing school for a year and she was still learning languages. When she returned from France, he had put her on show, dressing her in the height of fashion, having her entertain for him and taking her everywhere for a few weeks. No one had known of the ever lengthening periods she had spent in a remote cottage on Exmoor while Gilda had taken her place with Philip in his Caribbean retreat.

Philip had been a good-looking, active man, despite his age. Lisa had been full of apprehension when she married him but he had promised he would never touch her and he had kept his word. She hadn't dared ask why he never took advantage of what would have been his normal rights as a husband but once, in a rarely sentimental mood, he had told her that in the whole of his life he had only been attracted to two women. One was Gilda, the other he had never named.

But, for all his discretion, the press had eventually sensed a mystery—if they had never got to the bottom of it, and Lisa had been the natural and innocent victim. There was a lot of speculation over the increasingly wild parties Philip had started to give, on Gilda's instigation. It was believed that Lisa was responsible for them, while in reality she had protested each time Philip had forced her to attend them, but when the press had cornered her, she had never been able to deny some of the comments they had thrown at her as this would have meant betraying him.

She had begun to feel terrified, believing he might live for ever when, after her parents died, he refused to consider either a divorce or separation. Yet when he had died suddenly, soon after her father, the relief she had experienced had left her with a feeling of guilt she couldn't get rid of. Edward, when she had, in desperation, confessed this to him, had told her she was being ridiculous, especially when Philip, apart from keeping her, had never given her any money or left her anything. If it hadn't been for Edward, she wouldn't even have got the miserable house and few pounds a week, which was all he had managed to save from Gilda's greedy clutches. Her guilt, however, was still with her.

Alex, though, only needed to know that the stories about her, regarding other men and wild parties weren't true. She could easily prove this by sleeping with him but this she wouldn't do! If he persisted in seeing her again, she must try and convince him by talking to him. If this failed there was nothing more she could do.

It was Saturday and she tidied the house listlessly. Later she would shop for food for the weekend but her lack of appetite didn't encourage her to hurry.

About eleven the telephone rang and she picked it up nervously. She thought it might be Alex and wasn't sure if she was relieved when Edward spoke.

'Hello, Lisa,' he said, 'I hope I haven't woken you up?'

'You should know me better than that!' she replied, trying to sound amused.

'I thought perhaps after the late night you'd had?' he teased.

How did he know about that? The newspapers? Her hands dampened with the quick perspiration which even the thought of the gossip columns could bring. 'What late night?' she asked cautiously.

He laughed, a kindly chuckle she couldn't take exception to. 'Alex Andreas told me.'

'Alex.' She relaxed, yet tensed.

'You're on more friendly terms?'

'I'm not sure,' she prevaricated, 'but, surely, he didn't ring you up to discuss our evening out?'

'Hardly,' Edward said. 'He wants the papers about the island signed. He implied you'd agreed.'

'Even so, couldn't it wait until Monday?'

'With most people it would have to,' Edward sighed. 'I can't, however, afford to offend him. It's not just him, it's the influence he has. But don't get me wrong, Lisa,' he hastened to add, 'he is an admirable man and seems to think a lot of you.'

'So much,' she mocked, though her heart missed a beat, 'that he has to interrupt my weekend because of business?'

'I tried to put him off.'

'It's all right,' she gave in, 'I wasn't doing much, anyway, and I know you'd have done your best. Where am I to meet him? At your office?'

'No, at his penthouse,' Edward explained, 'and he wants me along as well, so I'll pick you up.'

It was a nuisance. The more she thought of it, the more certain she became that Alex was playing some devious game of his own. Indignation made her dress casually, a pair of jeans, thin blue top and light jacket. The morning was fine and not cold but she mistrusted the few clouds about.

She didn't feel like facing Alex so soon but if Edward was there and it was only about Enos, it might be better to get it over and done with. With that behind them, if Alex still wished to see her, at least she would know his interest was personal.

Edward picked her up promptly at almost the minute arranged. She smiled at him warmly, thinking how reassuring he was with his sleek silver hair and kindly expression. He was so dependable and had seen her through so much, yet he was no country bumpkin, if such a person still existed or ever did. He was a fund of sharply intelligent advice which had helped her to carry on many times when she might have given up.

Today, he glanced at her carefully as she sat beside him, looking so young and beautiful, with her wonderful fair hair and wide, trusting blue eyes, that his heart swelled with affection. There was brief anxiety, too, and something wary in his glance that caught her attention.

'Is there something wrong, Edward?' she asked.

'Quite the reverse,' he said, after a barely noticeable hesitation. 'I'm completing a deal which could have been awkward.'

'Awkward?'

'If you had decided not to sell.'

'If Enos had been how I imagined it would be, I shouldn't have done.'

'But you might have taken more time to consider? You might even had decided on another visit, which wouldn't have pleased Andreas.'

'And you feel that's necessary,' Lisa observed tartly.

'Diplomatically, yes.' He grinned. 'But he isn't such a bad sort, Lisa, once you get to know him. He's a bit overwhelming, I admit, but, as I mentioned before, he does seem to like you.'

'Our friendship,' Lisa couldn't stop her soft mouth twisting, 'had rather a stormy beginning. I don't think he is sure how he feels about me. I shouldn't be surprised if he secretly considers me a pest.'

'Not from what I gather,' said Edward with amusement.

Lisa digested this in silence. Was Edward match-making? At times he had been infuriated by the barrenness of her marriage to Philip and, she knew, terribly sorry for her and all she had to put up with, but surely he wasn't suggesting she might marry again?

Could she face another marriage? Maybe—eventually. Her smooth brow creased. But re-marriage would not be to a man like Alex Andreas. He would demand too much of her and she shrank from the publicity that even being friends with him would bring.

A little heat crept into her cheeks and she turned her head to look at the busy pavements so that Edward wouldn't see. Alex Andreas attracted her, she couldn't deny it. When he kissed her, he stirred up feelings she hadn't known existed and, as well as that, she was somehow drawn to him. If he stopped seeing her it would take her a long time to forget him, but, she reasoned, far better an immediate severance than a later one which might be far more painful.

Alex's penthouse, she wasn't surprised to discover, was situated in one of the most prestigious parts of the West End. As Edward negotiated their entry into the block of luxurious dwellings, she wondered how many such places in different countries Alex had, and how often he lived in them.

He let them in himself, dressed in a pair of jeans very like her own, only a much larger size. In them, he reminded her very much of how he had looked on the island and she drew a sharp breath. The black leather belt he wore with them might have been the very one which had bit into her waist when he had drawn her so ruthlessly into his arms and kissed her. There were no servants to be seen, although one practically followed them into the lounge with a tray of coffee.

'I thought you might like to have something immediately,' he smiled, removing her jacket and to her surprise bending to kiss her mouth warmly. 'Good morning, Lisa. You look delightful.'

If he had to kiss her, why hadn't he done so as soon as she arrived on his doorstep? Did he never act conventionally? Aware of Edward's interested glance, she smiled coolly, ignoring the inner turmoil that Alex seemed able to reduce her to with such ease.

'I'd appreciate some coffee,' she agreed, remembering she'd had no breakfast and suddenly feeling thirsty. 'It was kind of you to think of it.'

He grimaced as she sat down, commenting with dry impatience, 'You don't have to sound like a schoolgirl out for a treat when you come here. Even if,' his eyes rested mockingly on her swinging plait, 'you sometimes remind me of one.'

She flushed at the swift disappointment that rushed through her, suddenly conscious that the last way she wished him to think of her was as a schoolgirl. After he poured her coffee, she helped herself to cream and glanced idly at the open newspaper lying on the coffee-table, as he spoke to Edward.

'Oh, no!' Her shocked, involuntary exclamation turned the heads of the two men abruptly towards her but she didn't notice. She was too busy staring at the photograph on the centre page. There she was, in Alex's arms, which would have been bad enough in itself, but the photograph cleverly suggested the kind of intimacy which she was sure, give the devil his due, Alex had never intended. Then, adding horror to horror, Lisa suddenly realised it was she, more than Alex, who might be responsible for such an impression. Something about her body, the way it curved and clung to him, clearly implied she was the kind of woman who wouldn't be the least embarrassed about being caught with a man in that position . . .!

Tears rushed to her eyes and she blinked them away but her coffee cup positively rattled in its saucer as she tried to put it down. If it hadn't been for Alex's prompt action it would have spilt.

'Steady!' he rasped, his voice curt but concerned. 'Lisa, what's wrong? Is it—Ah!' His glance followed her horrified one to the paper. 'I see.'

She clenched her teeth, wanting to throw abuse at him for daring to expose her to that kind of thing, but remembering how futile anger had been in the past, she managed to control herself a little.

'Did you have to leave it there,' she accused, her face white, 'where you knew I might see it?'

He didn't offer an apology. 'I'll admit I was looking at it but I had forgotten about it. That's how much it bothers me.'

She couldn't understand such heartless indifference. 'You know it bothers me . . .'

'You will have to grow a thicker skin.'

Edward intervened gently. 'Lisa has suffered a lot from this kind of thing, Alex. I had hoped she wouldn't see this morning's papers.'

Alex frowned as he glanced back at Lisa. 'Last night, I thought you were overwrought and the press had merely caught you in a bad mood. You've been so much in the news in the past that I couldn't believe you were that sensitive about it, but if it really upsets you I'll certainly put a stop to it.'

'Lisa doesn't deserve the publicity she has had,' Edward said grimly.

That Alex merely shrugged to this, didn't make Lisa feel any happier. Dully she watched him pick up the newspaper unconcernedly and walk to the other side of the room where he dropped it into a drawer. Then, going to the bar in the corner, he selected a bottle and filled a glass. Returning to Lisa, he sat down beside her consideringly and gave it to her.

'Brandy,' he said briefly, noting her continuing tension with another frown. 'Drink it up, there's a good girl, and your coffee. Forget the newspapers, leave them to me.'

The glint in his eyes, convincing her that she could, made her shiver as she realised he would be a harsh man to cross. Obediently she sipped the brandy, dismayed, as it helped her to pull herself together, at the fuss she had made. She only wished Edward had warned her about the photograph, instead of trying to protect her from it.

Alex watched her closely as she swallowed her drink and if his brows rose a little when she choked, he made no comment. It wasn't until after she had finished that he said to Edward, 'You have the agreement with you?' Then, when Edward nodded, 'As Lisa has agreed to sell, let's get it over with.'

Lisa couldn't have agreed more. She still felt shaky and her head ached—she would be glad to get home again.'

Edward carefully produced some printed forms from his briefcase. After letting Alex see them, he placed them neatly before Lisa. 'This is where you sign,' he said, handing her a pen and indicating a dotted line.

About to write her signature, Lisa paused to glance over the legal jargon which covered the sheets and her eyes widened as they fell on the quoted figure.

'You tricked me!' she exclaimed, looking from Edward to Alex angrily. 'I never agreed to this ridiculous price. I won't be put under an obligation to anyone—or treated like charity.'

'Lisa!' Alex sounded just as angry. 'I'm not trying to do either of those things.'

'Maybe not,' she retorted sharply, forgetting Edward who didn't try and intervene. 'I'm aware that if I accepted this it wouldn't give you a hold over me but I wouldn't feel right about it.'

'Why not?' Alex argued tersely. 'It's me, isn't it? You know I want you and you're fighting the same feelings in yourself. You aren't being logical, Lisa. Enos has nothing to do with the relationship between you and me. Once you have signed that paper, you don't need to think of it again and the money will set you up for life. You can give Philip's money to charity.'

'Look.' Edward coughed, calling their attention to him, looking slightly amused. 'I know I'm here as your legal adviser but I think you might fight this out better by yourselves. You know my views, Lisa, but I know how stubborn you can be.' To Alex, he added, 'If she does sign, send it on to me—if she doesn't then I'll amend it according to what you decide.'

Lisa would have gone with him but he left while she was still trying to find her coat.

'Leave it,' Alex rapped shortly, returning from seeing Edward out, as she discovered it by the side of a chair. 'Sterne has gone but you are staying. Whatever the outcome of that,' he waved a frustrated hand towards the form on the table, 'we are spending the day together.'

Lisa, feeling unaccountably hurt by the condemnation in his eyes, said haltingly, 'I know you're annoyed with me, Alex, but if you alter the price I'll sign it tomorrow.'

'Can't bear to feel indebted to me, can you?' he snapped. 'All right, I'll get Edward to draft a new agreement but the next time I ask you to agree to something I hope you won't be so reluctant.'

Her heart warmed as the renewed confidence in his voice played on her imagination. He could be thinking of many things, even marriage? Then she told herself sternly not to be so ridiculous. It was probably the last thing on his mind and, anyway, she'd had enough of marriage with Philip. She ignored a voice that whispered that with another man it could be different.

Nevertheless, she smiled shyly at Alex as he dropped down beside her, her former antagonism fading. 'If you please me,' he muttered, pulling her against him, 'you won't ever be short of money again. I can give you everything any woman could possibly need.'

Lisa tried to move away from him, her wariness of him returning. She wasn't sure she liked the sound of that. He still seemed to be going too fast.

'Lisa?' He merely tightened his arms as she wriggled and lifted her chin as she frowned. 'Do we have to wait until everything is signed, sealed and delivered, in black and white? I'm sure you aren't that cruel.'

Was he talking of a pre-marital relationship? Her heart lurched. She thought Greeks didn't believe in that sort of thing but this might only be in their own country. 'You have to give me time,' she murmured, thinking this was the safest kind of answer until she was surer of what he meant.

He stared into her guarded eyes, his own intent. 'I know I promised you more time, last night, but sometimes things happen so quickly that the people involved don't always find it necessary.'

Lisa sat very still. Could such a thing happen to her? She knew that after knowing Alex nothing would ever be the same for her again. There seemed an absolute rightness about being with him but was she ready yet to commit herself blindly to whatever he was asking? She was acting as if she were in love with him, she thought in horror, which had to be impossible as they were still practically strangers.

'What is it?' he asked, when she didn't reply and her slender body trembled. 'Why do I frighten you, Lisa, because you are afraid of me, aren't you? I feel it whenever I have you in my arms. Your heart flutters like that of a bird I once caught, when I was a boy.'

'Did you let it go?' she whispered, feeling she might be sharing a similar experience.

'I let the bird go, yes, but,' he paused, looking deep into her eyes so she should know he had guessed what she was thinking, 'I will never release you. Now will you tell me why you're so frightened?'

How could she tell him anything? He would never understand the sheer terror that sometimes beset her whenever she considered the possibility of committing herself to another man. Not that Philip had been actively unkind, apart from threatening her with the unwanted attentions of his friends, but four years spent wondering when his threats would turn into reality had

left their mark. Even if she did marry again, she feared
that the scars Philip had left her with might prevent her
from being able to be a normal wife, and if Alex was
thinking of becoming her next husband, she could
imagine his anger and disappointment. If she failed to
please him sexually, he might never forgive her.

Miserably, she shook her head, as Alex still stared at
her enquiringly. 'I think the way I feel has something to
do with my marriage . . .' she began helplessly. 'I don't
think I can explain.'

'Why not?' he asked impatiently.

'I don't know . . .' She blinked into the black eyes
with eyes which suddenly seemed too big for her face
and with a muffled growl, he drew her gently against his
shoulder.

'Now,' he said softly, 'tell me.'

'I can't!' she insisted.

He sighed, his breath stirring her hair. 'Edward did
warn me you were stubborn. Something's wrong and if
you won't tell me, I'm going to have to use some other
method of persuasion.'

His strong hands touched her neck then moved on to
her nape. His lips followed as he pushed the collar of
her shirt aside and pressed kisses on her bare skin,
making her quiver. Then his lips slid along her jaw, and
he turned her face up so her mouth could meet his and,
almost imperceptibly, his warm, rapid kisses changed
into slow, sensual ones.

Involuntarily, as something like fire shot through
Lisa's senses, her hands slipped around his waist. She
had meant to fight him but before she could, her whole
body seemed consumed by impossible yearnings. Her
eyes closed tightly and the heat and darkness began
blending in wild, incredibly sweet sensation which made
a mockery of her previous suspicion that she wasn't
normal.

Yet, in a strange way, the very force of her feelings
brought a different kind of fear, as they made her

realise just how vulnerable she had become to the man holding her. Somehow she managed to gather enough control to stiffen against him and, surprisingly, he seemed to guess what she wanted and let her go. But as he fell to watching her again, as she gulped air, she knew he was still waiting for an explanation, and that explaining her secret phobias and protesting her innocence wasn't going to protect her from Alex at all. Something in his black, predatory glance told her he still wanted her and until she decided what to do about it, she had to think of some means of protecting herself. Perhaps, until she could see things clearer, it might be better to let him think she had been roughly handled by men and was scared of them?

'You were right,' she murmured. 'There is something wrong but I don't want to talk about it.'

'You'll have to one day,' he said gently, though his eyes hardened. 'Facing up to a phobia is the only way. No good ever came of hiding at home like a coward. You've got to get out and meet people again. You may not have Philip to protect you now, but you have me.'

'I'll try, Alex,' she promised uncertainly, feeling driven to say something to satisfy him.

'We'll succeed,' he murmured enigmatically, drawing her back to him and availing himself once more of her trembling lips. His kiss ignited the fires she was coming to be afraid of as she was terrified of being burned. His hand sought the softness of her breast while the other moved restlessly on her thigh. She could almost feel the passion mounting in his powerful body which had probably never known what it was to be deprived.

'I'll make you want me, Lisa,' he muttered, his eyes glowing like hot coals as she stirred uneasily against him. 'You won't go on refusing me.'

'Alex . . .'

'Come on,' he gritted, ignoring her protesting plea as

he stood up and dragged her up with him then steered her towards the door. 'Let's get out of here, my darling, for if we stay, there's only one place we're going to end up spending the day!'

CHAPTER FIVE

ALEX was so sure she would eventually give in to him that during the following days Lisa clung to the fictitious protection she had contrived for herself. In the two weeks which followed her first visit to his London penthouse, he had taken her everywhere. There wasn't a single evening when they hadn't enjoyed some form of entertainment. They attended concerts and plays, dined and danced together and took advantage of the lengthening spring evenings to drive into the country. Twice he had taken her to parties given by some of his friends and each Sunday he lunched with her. On all these occasions Alex had paid her the closest attention and, perhaps because of this, as he had predicted, her courage slowly returned and with it a new confidence.

When Philip had been with her at parties, always devoting himself more to Gilda than his wife, Lisa had been too conscious of the malicious whispering to enjoy herself. Like all spiteful gossip, it had rarely been on the side of the innocent. 'What else could a little gold-digger expect, marrying a man so much older,' she had heard more than one party guest comment. There had been more disparaging remarks when Philip began introducing her to well known rakes in order to cloak his own discreditable behaviour. Of course people had rarely criticised Philip. It had been Lisa who had borne the brunt of their contempt.

Once it became known that Alex Andreas was interested in her, this state of affairs, which had continued with astonishing tenacity since Philip's death, changed quite dramatically. Alex let it be known, subtly, that he wouldn't countenance it. In fact, he appeared to take pleasure in catching a derisive glance directed at Lisa and outstaring it. Few, Lisa had noticed with awe then some misgivings, could sustain the lethal contemplation in Alex's black eyes when he was standing over her like a watchful tiger.

If this was all there had been to their friendship, Lisa might have been content but though he didn't pester her with over-intimate advances, she was well aware that he didn't believe she would resist him for long. One evening, as he kissed her good night, he had told her thickly that anticipation was all that was keeping him going. He had smiled but Lisa had known he wasn't joking.

The sensible thing to do would be to put him out of her life, but, even if he allowed it, she wasn't sure she would be able to. Despite herself, she found herself growing more and more attached to him and she still hoped that their mutual attraction might deepen into something meaningful, though she never allowed herself to be more explicit.

This evening, Alex was giving a larger than usual cocktail party at his penthouse. Having been held up over a business deal, he was late in coming for her and they returned to find that some of his guests had already arrived. The secretary he employed in the UK had let them in and was busily seeing to the provision of drinks. Lisa was immediately the focus of everyone's eyes as she and Alex walked in. Alex had an arm firmly around her waist and, whatever construction was put on this clearly possessive gesture, no one looked anything but pleasant. He removed her wrap himself, holding it for a moment, it seemed almost deliberately, before instructing a servant to take it to his bedroom.

Lisa began to relax, enjoying herself when she forgot her underlying tension. Alex's open possessiveness would have thrilled most women, it did her, to a certain extent, or it may have done if she had been able to ignore the questions to which she could find no answers.

The dress she was wearing, a flowing creation in white and silver, suited her but like many of the dresses that Philip had instructed a famous couturier to design for her, it was extremely provocative. She had decided to get rid of them until she realised they were necessary for her evening assignments with Alex. He demanded perfection and, if she failed to reflect it, it was quite conceivable that he would insist on buying her a new wardrobe himself. And further controversy about money was something she wished to avoid. It had been difficult enough when he had learned she had given the money he had paid her for Enos, to charity. He had practically accused her of preferring another man's money to his. When, in turn, she had accused him of being illogical, she had seen his eyes flash with an anger she had no wish to invite again.

This evening Lisa had brushed her hair into an abundance of curls and waves gleaming over her shoulders and the complementary perfection of her delicate, fine-boned features, above the sleek sophistication of her dress, made her irresistible. If she had doubted this, the frequently devouring intentness of Alex's glance would have reassured her.

She was surprised to find the other guests amazingly friendly. It could be partly due to Alex but they appeared to be discovering she had likeable qualities, and, despite her beauty, wasn't quite the femme fatale they had previously taken her for. Long ago, Lisa had learned how to make light, amusing conversation, but, this evening, for the first time in years, she found herself enjoying being with people.

Alex was with her when Gilda arrived. He must have felt her stiffen with shock for he looked at her sharply. He couldn't very well question her for the crowd around them and Lisa was grateful for the chance to compose herself, which she might not have had if they had been alone. She had no wish to give him the unguarded answers he might have been able to drag out of her, had they been alone, and she didn't want to discuss Gilda as she didn't think it would serve any useful purpose and might only revive everything she was trying to forget.

She had to reply when he murmured in her ear, though, 'Are you acquainted with Mrs Grant?'

Lisa nodded, regretting the distaste she wasn't quick enough to hide when his eyes narrowed suspiciously. 'Are you?' she asked, somewhat stupidly.

'I don't know her any better than I know half the people here,' he said enigmatically.

Taking her arm, he drew her gently over the room to greet Gilda and the party she had arrived with. Lisa saw the other woman's eyes cool malignantly at this evidence of the favour Lisa was rumoured to have found with the wealthy Greek. But, like Lisa, she merely smiled coolly, seemingly no keener than the girl before her to reveal how well they had known each other previously. Other guests watched curiously but soon lost interest as what a few privately thought might develop into a highly inflammable situation, came to nothing.

Lisa, believing Gilda would contrive to be on her best behaviour, did her best to ignore the disquiet she aroused in her, but, as the evening progressed, she knew she had to have a break from the increasing venom in Gilda's eyes as they followed her around. When Alex left her for a few minutes, to talk to some men, she swiftly escaped into his bedroom.

His bedroom was large but only her wrap lay on his bed. Lisa's heart began missing beats as she stared at it and her face flushed as she wondered what interpretation other people might put on it if they noticed it.

She didn't have to wonder long as the door opened quickly behind her and Gilda walked in. As her vicious eyes fell on Lisa's wrap, she exclaimed without preamble, 'So this is what you are up to, now!'

It sounded so like an attack that Lisa's flushed cheeks

immediately whitened. What right had Gilda to burst in on her like this and challenge her as if she was a criminal continuing a career of crime. The only thing she might have been guilty of was of countenancing Philip's duplicity long after she should have done. In that—in some way—she must have been as guilty as Gilda and Philip in deceiving Gilda's husband.

At least she was able to state with relative conviction, 'What I choose to do now, Gilda, has nothing to do with you.'

'You have money which should have come to me,' Gilda stated outrageously. 'You're a mercenary little bitch and I won't have another man fooled.'

'My God!' Lisa gasped. 'You have a nerve. Philip had very little to leave to me, you saw to that. I got an old terraced house which, as he sold the one belonging to my parents and forgot to hand over the money, was only fair. The few pounds a week he left me, I consider I'm entitled to for the sacrifices I made. As soon as I can do without it, I'm going to, but it won't be coming your way!'

Gilda snarled furiously. 'You know Philip adored me and promised I should have all he had. I've heard something about an island . . .'

Lisa's eyes widened. How did such things get around? She was sure neither Alex or Edward would have mentioned it. 'The proceeds have gone to charity,' she replied curtly.

'Charity! Why you little fool!' Gilda cried wildly. 'Philip would have wanted me to have it. He loved me!'

'I think the time is past for recriminations, Mrs Grant,' came Alex's voice from the doorway.

He must have entered silently. Both women swung about in dismay. Gilda was probably about the same age as Alex but her expression was so vindictive, she looked suddenly haggard and older.

'I'm merely having a little talk with Lisa, Mr Andreas,' she tried to bluff with amazing aplomb, once she was over her first shock.

'Not in my bedroom,' he retorted emphatically. 'Only Lisa is welcome here.'

'With all her experience of men's bedrooms,' Gilda sniped maliciously, 'it seems only right that someone should reap the benefit.'

While Lisa struggled with outraged breath, Alex went pale and his black eyes blazed murderously. 'I said you weren't welcome in my bedroom, Mrs Grant. I'd like to extend that to include the rest of my apartment. I'm asking you to leave immediately.'

Gilda stared at him, obviously wishing to defy him but not daring to. There was such bitter defeat in her face that Lisa might have felt sorry for her, if she could have believed that one such set-back would bother her, once she got over it.

As the door closed behind her, Alex turned to Lisa, his harshness swiftly replaced by concern. 'I don't think you will be troubled by her again, darling.'

'No.' Lisa swallowed. 'And I'm grateful.'

'Prove it. At least try to,' he commanded, reaching for her, pulling her towards him derisively.

'Not this way,' she protested unsteadily, shattered from her confrontation with Gilda and distrusting the suddenly shuttered expression on his face.

'This is the only kind of recompense I'm interested in,' he said thickly. 'I'm in a sorry state when I have to find an excuse to kiss you but don't look so surprised. You put yourself at my mercy, did you not, by coming to my bedroom? And the way you look tonight, would test the endurance of a better man then me.'

Lisa might have been amused by the righteousness in his voice if she hadn't been so conscious of the fire his lips were igniting in her blood as they touched her cheek. She was aware that the dress she wore, with its thin bodice lovingly emphasising the generous curves of her breasts, was enough to excite any man. If she had wanted to, she could probably have found something less inciting, but always, despite the resolutions she made to try and encourage him to see less of her, she contrarily found herself dressing to attract him. Alex had saved her from Gilda but he wasn't offering comfort. Yet even the dark, rich sound of his voice wove a heated spell which the love she was beginning to feel for him was only too eager to respond to. As he enclosed her in the prison of his arms she longed to cling to him but forced herself to remember the heartache she could be inviting if he intended merely playing with her.

'Alex,' she pleaded, 'let me go. You have guests . . .'

'What of it?' he growled, dismissing her plea as firmly as he grasped her chin and turned her mouth up so he could close his own over it. His tongue dived, tangling with hers, scattering all further protest from her head. Dazed, her mouth slackened and she let herself drift on the tide of their rising desire until she was conscious of nothing but the stultifying waves of it.

How long they remained locked together like this, she had no idea. Alex was lightning and storm cloud, full of elemental powers. He possessed a primitive masculine sensuality, a lightly leashed savagery, that a hitherto unsuspected feminine counterpart deep within Lisa both longed and feared to release. Wildly she clung to him, wanting to offer everything yet hoping to satisfy him with the sweetness of her lips.

Without hesitation he took even this much as her surrender. His kisses became deeper and hungrier as he pressed them ravenously over her face and neck. It wasn't until he slipped the narrow straps off her shoulders and his hands sought her breasts that she grew frightened and began to fight.

Her ineffectual struggles ground their hips together and Lisa ceased her writhing abruptly when she realised he was enjoying and responding to the stimulation of her squirming body. She parted her lips, now desperate to use the only weapon that seemed left to her—words. It came to her uneasily that she would have been wiser

to have told Alex the truth about the experience she had
let him believe she'd had with other men. 'Alex,' she
breathed, as his mouth sought her distended nipples.
'No!'

'Lisa,' he groaned, 'be quiet!'

'I can't,' she entreated. 'You have to listen.'

'If it's about that Grant woman,' he muttered
harshly, raising his head, 'you can forget it.'

Mechanically she shook her head. 'Gilda was Philip's
friend.'

Grim enlightenment dawned in his eyes. 'You mean
she was Philip's mistress. This was why you turned for
revenge to other men—and got more than you
bargained for!'

Lisa's eyes widened with horror that he should think
this. She had to tell him. 'Alex, those other men . . .'

'I don't want to know about them.' His voice
hardened. 'I realise I said you'd be better to talk about
them but I don't think I could face it. I'm not thinking
of what it would do for you, but what it would do to
me. In this, I'm probably as near to being a coward as
I'll ever be.'

'But . . .'

Swiftly he thrust a hand that wasn't gentle over her
mouth. 'The only way to shut you up!'

His roughness brought quick tears to her eyes. His
arms tightened but instead of forcing more kisses on her,
he merely held her to his pounding heart. 'Don't cry,
sweetheart,' he murmured contritely. 'I would never do
anything to hurt you, you know that. Nor hurry you, if
it's still time you must have. But when you come to me,
Lisa, I can assure you it won't be like it was with those
other men. I won't hurt you. I'll show you such
pleasure that you won't ever say no to me again.'

'You don't understand,' she whispered weakly.

'I do,' he muttered thickly, 'but I find I'd rather
forget about your past. No good might come of raking
it up. I get so damned jealous, I can't trust myself not

to say or do something which could make you hate me. As long as you learn you can trust me, that's all I ask.'

Lisa bit her lip. If he wouldn't listen, she couldn't make him, and she felt too resentful of his determined refusal to do so, to persevere. 'If you don't choose to listen, it's fine by me,' she said tersely. 'I can't see much future for us anyway.'

He laughed softly, refusing to take her quick anger seriously. 'You won't be saying that, once I get you in my bed, sweetheart. Your only concern then will be that I shouldn't leave you.' His black eyes glinted. 'Up till now, I've been very tolerant with you but my patience is running out. I won't force you, though, for I know that soon you will come to me willingly.'

Such arrogance stung and she jerked away from him as he complacently relaxed his guard. 'I'm not half as willing as you think!' she hissed, rushing to the door.

'We shall see,' he mused, following at a more leisurely pace but fast enough for one or two wandering guests to spot them emerging from his bedroom together. Lisa could have slain him when the conclusions they obviously leapt to only appeared to amuse him, instead of embarassing him as they did her.

Alex had to fly to Greece on urgent business for a few days. He had asked her to accompany him but she had refused, which hadn't pleased him. Despite this, flowers were delivered to her house each day he was away and he rang every morning and evening.

Lisa, having expected to enjoy the freedom of being without him for a while, was dismayed to find how much she missed him. She passed the time, while he was gone, giving a crash course in French to a desperate student. She did this to supplement her income until she got a full time job. The young man's parents were delighted with the results of her tuition and it was in this way, by personal recommendation, that she was able to get a steady flow of pupils. Usually they were short-term but she preferred this as it meant she could be free very quickly if anything more permanent came up.

She never talked to Alex about her work for she feared, if she did, he would only lecture her again about parting with the proceeds from the island. And she didn't want him to know how little Philip had left her.

When he returned and arranged to pick her up to take her out for dinner, she was ready when the doorbell rang. Deliberately, she had her wrap in her hand, so she wouldn't have to ask him in, but after bending to kiss her hungrily, he pushed her back inside.

'I'm ready to go,' she protested as he closed the door behind him, enclosing them in the intimacy she had been trying to avoid.

'I haven't seen you for five days,' he retorted huskily, his eyes feasting on her slender body and the soft, vulnerable look which always seemed such a contradiction of what he knew of her. He seemed lost for a moment in her eyes, and shuddered, as if merely to gaze into them sent tingles down his spine.

'Your skin's pale cream,' he said unsteadily. 'Flawless, extraordinary, like the colour of your mouth and eyes. I've a hunger I can't satisfy merely by looking at you in a restaurant. I have to have you in my arms.'

Lisa had tried to forget how handsome he was, how impressive with his height and broad shoulders, his lean but powerful hips. She had tried to forget how sensuous his mouth was, how white his teeth and dark his eyes and despaired to discover she had forgotten nothing.

'I think I—I'd rather go straight out,' she stammered, putting a hand to her heart which appeared to be doing acrobatics.

'And I would rather kiss you.' He grasped her shoulders, leaving her in no doubt as to who was going to win. 'I've also brought you a present.'

' A present?' she murmured uncertainly.

'So that intrigues you, does it?' The black eyes

glowed with satisfaction. 'Sometimes you surprise me, too, by responding like a normal woman.'

'I hope I am all the time,' she replied sharply, without betraying she was more apprehensive than intrigued.

He drew her closer, pressing light, restless kisses on her face. 'I don't think I can ever leave you again,' he growled, baring her shoulder to his ravaging mouth. Lisa gasped as he nuzzled her neck finding with his tongue the throbbing pulse at the base of her throat. Her words of protest slurred as she tried to speak and she only managed it with a great effort.

'Alex!'

'What is it?' He withdrew slightly, his eyes hot as she pushed against him agitatedly. 'Ah, you want your present first,' he smiled, again mistaking her reaction.

About to argue, it suddenly seemed easier not to. 'What is it?' She managed not to frown suspiciously. She had no wish to hurt him. If he had been kind enough to bring her something then surely she could accept it graciously? She tried to ignore the intuition which warned she wasn't going to like it.

His smile grew silky and laced with the arrogant confidence she was coming to expect from him. Sliding a hand into his pocket, he drew forth a long, flat box. 'Open it,' he instructed, giving it to her.

Lisa obeyed carefully. Even so, the brilliant flash of diamonds nearly blinded her. She wouldn't have liked to have put a price on the wonderful necklace lying sparkling on its bed of white velvet—diamond and sapphire necklaces weren't to be valued like a pound of butter, but this one might have been worth hundreds of thousands of pounds. The little she had learned of jewellery over the past few years, mostly through keeping her eyes and ears open, assured her she wasn't far wrong.

'You can't intend this for me?' she gasped.

'It's yours, I'm giving it to you.' He sounded so complacent, her blood boiled. 'As soon as I saw it, I knew it was just the thing for your beautiful neck.'

'I'd like to wring yours!' she retorted fiercely. 'You must have known I couldn't accept a gift like this! It must be worth a small fortune.'

'Must you always reduce things to terms of money?' he grated, eyes suddenly blazing. 'Why can't you take it? You must have accepted plenty of presents from other men.'

'No!' She glared, unconscionably hurt. 'It may surprise you to learn, I've never been in the habit. What do you take me for, Alex? Are you trying to buy me?'

To her surprise he muttered curtly, 'You wouldn't take what I offered for Enos.'

'So that's it?' she accused angrily. 'You're trying craftily to make me accept the difference.'

'I'd never be reduced to that,' he snapped, then sighed resignedly and removed the necklace from her numbed fingers, putting it aside to take her in his arms again. 'Don't you see . . .' he coaxed softly, 'I want to give you things but I'm not trying to buy you. When I take you it will be when you come to me willingly.'

'I shouldn't count on it,' she snapped into his persuasive face.

'You will.' His arms tightened roughly, his smile fading. 'Once I melt the ice you try and chill me with and once you stop deceiving yourself. Then you're going to forget that strange pride of yours . . .'

'Never!' she exclaimed, throwing back her head to convince him, which gave him the chance he was looking for.

His kiss wasn't as harsh as his voice had been. He didn't hurt her which briefly lulled away her fears and brought her to the brink of surrender. The half defeated sound that escaped her, parted her lips, inviting invasion, and his searing, mastering mouth shattered her remaining defences with shafts of pure sensation. As the pressure of his mouth deepened, hers softened and yielded beneath his demand for complete submission.

Weak and breathless, she lay limp against him,

defeated by the extreme urgency of his kisses. Slowly his hold on her gentled but his tenderness proved even more dangerous than his impatience, especially when she hadn't seen him for days. She trembled that she couldn't hide the strength of her need from him—or her love—while she was terrified of admitting either, even to herself.

He was keeping a tight rein on his passion but when Lisa tensed in his arms it immediately enraged him. Ruthlessly he swept her up and carried her to the lounge.

'If I seem to be making a habit of this,' he snapped, 'you have only yourself to blame.'

She struggled, reluctant to recall what had happened the last time he had carried her here but he took no notice.

'You want me,' he growled grimly. 'Why deny it?' Dropping her on to the sofa, he came down beside her, almost crushing her with his weight.

She had to deny it and tried to believe she was speaking the truth, even as every pulse in her body shrieked that she wasn't. With a mocking laugh, he twisted sideways to seek the taut swell of her breasts and she sighed as his thumbs taunted the hardening nipples under the thin material of her dress. Her eyes widened with dazed pleasure at the feelings this evoked, her pupils dilating until the blue all but overshadowed the irises.

Lisa trembled and a helpless moan escaped her. It was still new to her, this surging, frightening excitement she felt whenever Alex touched her—the indescribable promise of a rapture more devastating than anything she had ever dreamed of. Her head fell back as desire streaked along her veins until her whole body was aflame with it. Eventually when she could bear his goading caresses no longer, she turned her mouth up involuntarily to his.

He kissed her with a sudden violence and Lisa felt

herself drowning in the sensual response this aroused. Drawing a choked breath, she twined her arms around his neck, trying to get closer, the whole of her aching with a hunger she didn't understand but couldn't ignore. She suddenly longed to have the warmth and length of his body covering hers. He looked so magnificently savage, stripped of all his usual civilised control. He wasn't trying to hide the triumph in his eyes but she scarcely saw it for the haze of answering desire in her own.

Then he relaxed, making an almost obvious effort to ease the tension from his muscles. Slowly he drew her dress over her shoulders, taking care not to frighten her. As he slid it down to her waist, the black lace of her bra remained her only covering and he stared at her with burning eyes, devouring the sheer perfection of her body. His hands shook as he unhooked the clasp of her bra and flung it away before bending to explore the exposed, rosebud peaks with his mouth, searing them with its heat.

The expertise of his movements might have stunned her but she had neither the will or ability to fight. With breathless gasps, her fingers clenched then she pushed them through his black hair as the fire spreading through her sensitised body melted every bit of her resistance. She wanted him completely—if he had asked, and she had been able to answer, she wouldn't have disputed it any longer. She was like a cauldron, overflowing with cravings she didn't recognise but was eager to taste. When he moved fully over her, letting her feel how much he desired her, she thought she might faint from the overwhelming feelings this evoked.

'Let me stay with you tonight, darling,' he begged, as she breathed in the hot dampness of his skin. His voice was so thick with passion that she trembled. 'We can have a sandwich later but, right now, I'm only hungry for this.'

'Alex . . .'

'You don't have to be afraid, Lisa,' he groaned. 'I

won't hurt you or let anything happen to you. You will see how wonderful it can be.'

Lisa shivered. She didn't doubt him but his words worried her, cutting through the eagerness of her response like a sword. They scattered the prevailing ecstasy from her mind and replaced it with thoughts she had forgotten. If she gave in to him now, he would know as soon as he possessed her that she was a virgin, and she also knew that such a discovery would not impress him. He believed her an experienced woman and when he discovered she wasn't, he might accuse her of trying to trap him. And if all he wanted was an affair with her, he might send her away.

Suddenly Lisa felt, in her disorientated state, it was a risk she couldn't take. Yet how would he take another refusal? Why didn't she have the courage just to finish with him? It could be far less painful, in the long run.

'No, Alex,' she pleaded, eyes clouding with fear of his anger. 'I can't . . .! At least not yet. Please don't ask me.'

Seeing the sudden tears on her cheeks, his face miraculously softened. Instead of being angry, he mopped them up gently with his mouth and, after coming to terms with his own urgent needs, sighed resignedly.

'I can wait—not much longer, but I'll spare you this time. Just don't think about putting me off indefinitely, and when you do give in to me, I promise you won't regret it.'

The feelings still consuming Lisa made her feel she could believe him. It was later, when she was alone, that doubts again attacked her. He could show her a glimpse of a heaven she knew nothing about, he would be a confident and considerate lover, but what of afterwards? Once she belonged to him, would she be able to keep him captivated? If she belonged to him, without the ties of marriage, though he may have this in mind, might he not lose interest? If this happened how could she possibly bear it? Would it not be far more sensible to do without something she had never had than to spend her life consumed by regret and heartache?

After Lisa had tidied herself, they drove to a quiet restaurant and ate a belated dinner. Neither of them had much appetite but Alex, concerned by the delicate paleness of Lisa's face, insisted on going out. Afterwards they danced but he only held her lightly, as if he was resolved to do nothing more to disturb her.

For the next few weeks he continued his restraint and Lisa could find nothing to complain of in his behaviour. Yet though he took her out just as frequently and didn't attempt to get her to accept any more expensive presents, she had sometimes a niggling suspicion that he was simply biding his time, rather than turning over a new leaf.

Whether it was genuine or not, she soon realised the hidden dangers of his more circumspect behaviour. Perhaps because she missed the searing kisses she had grown used to, there was a temptation to cling to him too closely when he wished her a brief good night. Sometimes she felt such a bewildering sense of frustration that she despised herself. It filled her with self-contempt that she hadn't the courage to be honest with either Alex or herself about the desires which began constantly to plague her and wouldn't let her rest.

The strain, inevitably, began to tell on them both. For several days, now, he had showered her with extra attention, as if he couldn't help himself, but had grown more and more introspective. When he collected her, one evening to take her to a party a business friend of his was giving, he kissed her cheek lightly then pushed her away so abruptly she flinched.

'Alex, what is it?' she asked, alarm flashing through her as his face darkened.

'Nothing,' he replied tersely.

She was foolish enough to persist. 'It doesn't seem like nothing to me.'

'Forget it,' he snapped, his eyes restless. 'Unless you've suddenly discovered the meaning of frustration?'

'Oh.' She flushed as he hurried her out to his car. Sometimes for days he scarcely touched her and she had begun to feel he didn't want her anymore. Lately he had never forced the pace but seemed willing to let their friendship ripen slowly. She had been under the impression that there was no hurry but she wondered now if she hadn't been mistaken. Maybe her suspicions regarding his recent conduct had been closer to the mark than she had thought?

The party they were attending was held in the stockbroker belt of the city. The house was detached, with extensive grounds and full of beautiful, sophisticated people. Lisa saw several whom she knew and when Alex drifted away from her, she began talking to some of them.

Alex usually talked to other men though he was acquainted with plenty of women. Lisa watched his progress across the room uneasily without seeming to. She wasn't sure what the tension between them had aroused in him, this evening, but, for the first time since she had known him, he made staight for another woman.

Lisa closed her eyes briefly, feeling suddenly faint. For her, the stress of the past weeks had resulted in a lack of appetite and sleeplessness. For Alex, it must have been much harder. He wasn't used to women defying him and having to control his natural impulses.

From under her lashes, sick at heart, Lisa observed several things. She saw, if he was suffering from prolonged abstinence, that he had found someone to help him to relieve it. The woman he approached was as dark and beautiful as he was himself. She had long black hair and smoky eyes which seemed to smoulder as she talked to him. When they danced together, they were equally absorbed in each other.

So this was it! Lisa found she couldn't stay and watch. Whether Alex was serious about this other woman or not, she had to have time to get used to the idea that it was possible. She had half expected it for a while yet to find it actually happening was still a shock.

She escaped to the gardens, pretending she was going to the cloakroom. For perhaps fifteen minutes she wandered about without feeling any better. Some things had to be faced, and she might eventually achieve some sense of acceptance out here, but it came to her at last that it would take more time than a few minutes in a strange garden to accept the loss of Alex completely.

Getting a little lost, she hesitated in the moonlight, rounding the corner of a thick hedge. Then she drew back with a wounded gasp. Alex was standing at the other side of it, only a few feet away, his arms around the woman he had been dancing with.

CHAPTER SIX

LISA felt sickened and shocked and if she was looking for confirmation of Alex's unfaithfulness, she was given it in those few moments that she stood there, stunned into immobility.

The woman's voice came huskily. 'Darling, I've missed you. Four years is a long time.'

'Too long,' Alex agreed softly. 'But then a woman as beautiful as you must have met other men?'

'No one like you,' murmured the husky voice. 'I care for you, darling, that's the difference. I want you.'

'Now?' Alex's tones seemed to deepen.

There was a short silence when Lisa's despairing suspicion that he was kissing the woman and about to make love to her was confirmed by the woman's low triumphant laughter.

Lisa choked and ran, regardless of the betraying crunch of gravel under her feet. Rushing back to the house, her mind was whirling. She would have left the party straight away but she was on the outskirts of London with no transport, and she had no wish to draw attention to herself by asking someone other than Alex to take her home. Maybe later, she could plead a headache and ring for a taxi.

She found a drink and swallowed it and was grabbing another when Alex caught up with her.

'Lisa!' He grasped her arm with fingers which would leave a mark. 'Where the hell have you been?'

Fearing she was going to be sick, Lisa swallowed whatever was in her throat while her heart behaved in a way which made her feel even worse. There was absolutely nothing in his voice to reveal he had seen her rush away from him in the gardens, but somehow she was sure he had.

Looking at him, her eyes huge and haunted in her arrestingly beautiful face, she gambled that he couldn't know for certain it had been her. 'What a question,' she mocked. 'Shouldn't I be the one asking that?'

'Shut up!' he ground between his teeth. 'I have to talk to you.'

'I'm listening,' she said coolly.

'Not here,' he said forcefully. 'Come with me.' When she made no move to obey, he shot a steely arm around her waist, compelling her to.

They were leaving the room when all pretence of composure fell from her and she pleaded unevenly, 'I don't want to go to the gardens again.'

'So it was you!' His arm tightened about her. 'In here.' He closed the door of the library behind them. 'We shouldn't be disturbed.'

'Is there any special reason why we shouldn't be?' she muttered defiantly, blinking back tears.

'Lisa?' He watched sharply as the painful colour rose in her cheeks and frowned, for the first time since she had known him, seeming strangely at loss for words.

'Is that all you have to say?' she scorned, the numbness she still retained from the shock she had received on seeing another woman in his arms, enabling her to speak coldly.

'No.' Suddenly he moved restlessly, looking faintly embarrassed. 'You know it isn't. What you saw in the garden, Lisa, Carmel and me, there's nothing to get bothered about.'

'Bothered?' she blazed, walking angrily away from him and trying to concentrate on a painting over the fireplace, which had to be worth a fortune. With her back to him it was easier to exclaim, 'Why should I care what you do? There's nothing of a permanent nature about our relationship, is there? Is Carmel one of your past affairs or just a good bet for your next one?'

Each lethal word flayed like deliberately placed lashes

but she had only words which was perhaps why she used them so indiscriminately. His face went grey while his big body tensed and his strong features hardened. Then the opaque blackness of his eyes began blazing with a rage which made Lisa gulp with apprehension as his hands descended on her shoulders and he swung her back to him again. Before she could do anything to save herself, he shook her and didn't stop until her hair was tumbling about her face in wild disorder.

Then he jerked her into his arms and kissed her hard. When her weakening limbs must have indicated her strength was failing, he picked her up, apparently for the pleasure of throwing her down on the sofa and covering her shaking body with the vengeful weight of his own. When she made an abortive attempt to get away from him, frightened now of the anger relayed from his eyes and mouth, he held her close forcing her to lie still and look at him.

'Damn you!' he rasped harshly. 'How dare you say you don't care when I'm nearly driven out of my mind thinking about you. I'll make you care for me, if it's the last thing I do!'

With a furious breath, he renewed his brutal attack on her mouth, kissing her savagely and bringing a sharp flare of need. He paid no attention to her distress, his free hand wrenching open the fastening of her dress, and only then did his mouth leave hers to continue his ravaging attack on the softness of her breasts.

Lisa winced and fought against what he was doing to her. She wanted to scream and hit out at him, to abuse him with words, but she found she could do none of these things. His assault frightened her but what she hadn't expected was its physical effect. Suddenly she was clinging to him, matching his hard demands with a wild hunger of her own. As his mouth returned to hers, she trembled as his kisses grew deeper and she felt an ache of desire spread right through her. Feeling her response, his arms tightened roughly around her. He wanted her and nothing was going to stop him taking her this time. Then he raised his head and saw the tormented tears on her face.

His whole being underwent a change as he paused abruptly and stared at her. 'Lisa, oh my darling!' he entreated hoarsely. 'Don't cry, I can't bear it.'

She was so confused by the mixture of tears and passion inside her that she couldn't speak. Why did he hurt her if he couldn't bear to see her weep?

'Darling, please!' he groaned as her tears fell faster. 'I did mean to go as far as this but you're driving me insane. It's as well you got upset, though, for anyone might have come in. But you get me so I don't know what I'm doing.'

When he began tidying her dress, she flushed and tried to help him. 'Why?' she faltered.

'That's what I'm wondering myself, but I doubt if it's about the same thing. I'm wondering how you got such a hold on me?' Putting a hand under her chin, he made her look at him. 'I've had women in my bed before but never lodged in my mind, as you are. You're in there and I just can't get rid of you.'

'Do you want to?' she breathed.

'Do I want to?' he repeated, with returning harshness. 'God, what a question! Wouldn't any sane man wish to rid himself of something which gives him no peace, night or day?'

'Was this what you were trying to do when you were kissing Carmel?' she whispered bitterly.

'No—yes!' he growled. 'See how you tie me in knots.'

'You must have met her before,' Lisa retorted, painfully.

'Several years ago,' he admitted, 'but we didn't have an affair. We were together on a yachting party for a week, that's how long it lasted, and I hadn't laid eyes on her since.'

'Then, this evening, you wondered what you had missed?'

'No!' His eyes flashed angrily again then he collapsed against her with a groan. 'I thought I might make you jealous. She was willing enough, all smiles and melting looks, while you do nothing but glare at me and say no. For one crazy moment I thought she could give me some relief but as soon as I kissed her I knew it was no good.'

Despite this, Lisa felt unbearably hurt. 'You wanted to kiss her, though. How many women do you intend trying to find consolation with? Maybe the next one . . .?'

Abruptly, he countered. 'How many women have I taken out since I met you, darling? Don't I see you every evening?'

Yes, he did, and he seldom left her early. Even a man like Alex couldn't be that ingenious. She stirred uneasily in his arms but was reluctant to leave their comfort. How could she demand he remained faithful to her when she gave him so little? And, yet . . .

'What would you think if I went out with another man?' she asked.

'I'd kill him!' he scowled. 'I'd be so enraged I wouldn't be able to stop myself, so be warned. At least,' he added grimly, 'it couldn't be as bad as running away, like you did.'

She shivered, again seeing him with Carmel in the garden. 'I was jealous, too,' she confessed and, in a rush, 'I could have killed you out there, Carmel as well. I never remember feeling worse in my life.'

'Darling!' His eyes suddenly glowed. She had never betrayed more than a cool liking before. In spite of seeing each other all the time, he'd had no reason to believe her feelings were deeply involved and what she said seemed to reveal he was mistaken. 'Lisa?' he exclaimed hoarsely.

Lifting her eyes to meet the unspoken demand in his voice, her hands clenched tightly. He shifted his weight on her and she felt him shudder like a man with a fever.

'Confess,' he whispered thickly. 'Tell me exactly what you feel.'

She hesitated, her heart beating too heavily to make it easy to talk.

'Tell me,' he urged, bending to her lips.

Slipping her arms around his neck, she gave in. For weeks now she had guarded her innermost feelings from him, as her growing love for him had slowly conquered her ingrained inhibitions. Now she found she could no longer hide the truth. 'I love you,' she breathed against his mouth. 'I tried not to, but it just happened.'

He laughed, low and exultingly, crushing her to him. When she cried out he slackened his hold on her slightly but didn't apologise. His face was full of triumph as he kissed her eyes and nose and mouth. 'I didn't think I would ever hear you say it,' he gloated unashamedly. 'I worship you, you don't know how much. For weeks I've been driven mad with frustration, wanting you and hearing you refuse me, but you won't be able to refuse me after this, my darling. Before the night is out, you are going to belong to me—all of you!'

He sat up then lifted her to her feet, keeping a tight hold of her waist. 'Let's go,' he said huskily, 'I can't wait.'

Lisa shivered at the rawness of his voice. She felt her blood race as he gazed at her but she also felt apprehensive. He wanted her too much to allow her to escape, and now that she knew he loved her, she shared his sense of urgency, but she still couldn't help feeling uneasy.

Sensing her her inner tension, Alex pulled her closer. 'Forget those other men,' he murmured against her cheek. 'Think of me, how I've suffered the hell of frustration all these weeks, waiting for you to lose your fears. You'll have to trust me from now on, my darling, it's the only way.'

Reminded of how she had misled him about these other men, Lisa turned her face against his shoulder, realising she must somehow make him listen to the truth.

'I've never,' she began, only to find her voice cut off by his tightening grip, her words muffled before she could utter them.

'The time for talking is over, darling.' His fingers rubbed the back of her neck gently but firmly. 'I'll take care of everything, just leave it to me. Stay here and I'll find your wrap and we'll leave through the French windows. Eileen and Kurt are good friends of mine. I know my way about.'

As they drove back to London, Lisa sat in a daze. Alex always refused to listen but, she supposed dreamily, it must be rather wonderful that he loved her believing, as he had once implied, she was no better than she should be. If he loved her, believing this, how much deeper might his feelings for her be when he discovered she had never been with a man before? Of course a lot of men didn't worry over this kind of thing anymore, but Alex was a Greek and men of his nationality usually liked the girl they married to be completely innocent. Lisa couldn't help feeling that when he discovered she was, he would be pleased.

It wasn't easy to think of becoming Alex's lover before they were married but she guessed he would be making wedding plans immediately. She had always wanted to be married first, to the man of her choice, before belonging to him, but she loved Alex so much that this no longer seemed important. There would never be anyone else for her so how could she make a fuss about going to bed with him before the actual ceremony?

She was amazed at the difference their mutual baring of their feelings for each other had made. The searing awareness of each other was still there but she could sense a new satisfaction in Alex, a warm possessiveness which thrilled her. She met his smouldering glances frequently as they motored silently across London. She became lost in them, drugged by them, to the extent of being scarcely able to think.

He took her straight back to her own house. 'You can put this on the market any time,' he told her as he locked the door behind them. 'You will be moving in with me and won't need it.'

Her heart lightened against a returning nervousness and she nodded, feeling happier that he had mentioned it. She liked the house but parting with it would cause her no great heartache, and it was proof, if she needed any, that Alex's intentions were strictly honourable.

He didn't give her time to do more than nod as, once inside, he picked her up and carried her straight upstairs, pausing twice on the way to crush her mouth with passionate kisses. In her room, he didn't even bother to glance around but laid her down on the small double bed and began urgently undressing her.

His face was absorbed, his eyes never leaving her as he started undoing buttons and zips, his movements slowing as her dress dropped with a whisper of silk to the floor. She wore only two pieces of fragile underwear underneath and his eyes strayed on hers as he slid his hands over her before removing the flimsy garments.

'You're trembling,' he murmured.

'Yes.' Lisa swallowed. He didn't know she had never had a man in her bedroom before. It might have been easier if she and Philip had shared one but they never had. Incredible as it might seem, he had never once even entered her bedroom.

'Alex, wait,' she breathed, 'I have to explain . . .' Her voice came only in whispers but he had thrown off his own clothes and stopped her entreaties with a kiss.

'Not another word about that! All you have to remember is that I'm not going to hurt you. I'm going to make you mine, put my stamp on you, but you're only going to feel pleasure. There'll be no more pain.'

She could have insisted that he listened but he gave her no time, and with his mouth on hers she swiftly lost the thread of what she was saying. She had no immediate defence against the narcotic effect of his kisses. They wiped her mind clear of everything but the fires they lit inside her and she was too enveloped in their flames to worry anymore about something she had to tell him.

She moaned as he stretched out beside her and his kisses deepened as he felt her instant and complete response. Instinctively she knew he wanted to take her quickly and fiercely but when he drew away from her again she realised he was trying to restrain himself.

As he looked down on her, his shuddering breath filling the silence of the room, Lisa tilted her head back in blind supplication, seeing him hazily through the mist of her increasing desire, too vulnerable now to hide her own feelings. Alex was magnificently and passion-ately male and she wanted him very very badly. Her extremely sensuous nature, which had lain dormant until now, and which she had unconsciously been afraid of would, it seemed, be satisfied with nothing less.

With aching slowness he caressed the peaks of her breasts, murmuring words in Greek that made her want to weep for it was one of the languages she had never learned. She could feel her muscles contracting wherever he touched her, until her whole body was a mass of pulsating nerves. Her breathing became shallow and rapid as she was swiftly absorbed by his passion. She clung to him as his mouth continued its erotic penetration and he stroked her curves and soft hollows, seemingly careless that he was driving her insane.

Lisa gasped as her safe, ordinary world exploded about her, an intense excitement consuming her as he cupped her breast in his hand and caught a nipple between his teeth. She lay beneath him, her hair fanned around her, her mouth soft and trembling, her skin pink and warm. She was finding it difficult to stop her legs from entwining with his, she hadn't thought desire could be so overwhelming and, despite herself, her body began arching against his in a mute appeal as old as Eve.

She sensed the impatience in him and with an expertise she hadn't got, he recognised it in her. 'Are you ready?' he muttered thickly.

She could feel his heart thudding, his mouth moist and hotly demanding. She nodded, urging him closer, feeling the tremors passing through both of them, tremors that rendered her willing and helpless.

'You're sure?' He still hesitated. 'There's something about you . . .'

She guessed he sensed the lack of experience she had tried to tell him about. With the tip of his tongue he outlined her lips and she moaned and clutched his shoulders. She didn't want to talk about it now. 'When we are married . . .' she murmured.

She had no clear idea what she had been going to say and couldn't understand why he stiffened as though she had shot him.

'Marriage?' he exclaimed, staring at her blankly. 'Who said anything about marriage?'

'But—I thought . . .'

'Obviously far too much,' he snapped, pushing her away from him and whipping to his feet.

Lisa felt the chill starting in her body rapidly turning to ice. Alex's face, which only moments ago had been filled with the warmth of desire, had changed so much he looked an entirely different man. 'I b-believed,' she stammered pitifully, 'that marriage was what you had in mind.'

'My God!' his eyes glinted with scornful contempt, as he paced the room and returned to her. 'Your opinion of yourself, madam, transcends everything I ever heard of you. You must be mad!'

'Why?' She wished she could ask a more intelligent question but she was numb with shock. 'I thought you loved me.'

'You've obviously thought a lot of things,' he

retorted curtly, looming over her like a vengeful god, apparently uncaring that he was naked. 'Were you honestly convinced I would marry a woman like you?'

'L-like me . . .?'

'You lured your late husband into your bed and marriage, and heaven knows how many men since.' The arrogant lines of his face blurred with sudden rage. 'Did you imagine the same ruse would work with me? I'd as soon pick a woman from out of the gutter.'

Lisa's eyes smarted with pain and disillusionment. 'You believe I'm like them?'

'Your reputation proves it,' he replied scathingly, while a muscle leapt in his lean cheek as the sheet she had hastily covered herself with slipped and he caught an enticing glimpse of bare skin before she retrieved it again. 'I realised I was being led on by the nose but did you really think that by getting me to boiling point you would receive a proposal of marriage? The woman I'm going to marry will be nothing like you.'

'G-going to marry?'

'As soon as I decide and arrange it,' he said silkily. 'I've had someone in mind for quite a while. She will make me a good and dutiful wife, and, in return for my name and respect she will give me children.'

Lisa felt sure she was dying, bit by bit. Her voice trembled and her eyes seemed too huge for her face as she asked, 'Do you love her, Alex?'

'That's none of your business,' he rasped. 'I won't discuss her with you.'

'Well, your respect must be something,' she murmured bitterly. 'I suppose all we have left to say is goodbye. It's been nice knowing you, Alex,' she laughed almost hysterically. 'Now I'd appreciate it if you would just leave—get out of my bedroom!'

Without haste he picked up his clothes and began putting them on again. 'I might, for now,' he agreed suavely, 'but I wouldn't be too hasty, my dear. I'm still quite willing to accept you as my mistress.'

Lisa's stomach lurched violently. 'You have a nerve!'

He glanced at her cruelly as he thrust his feet in his shoes. 'I still want you, Lisa. Don't try and pretend you thought I wouldn't. And, as my mistress, you'd have just about everything you could wish for.'

'Apart from your name,' she exclaimed, through bloodless lips.

'Jewellery, apartments, money, clothes, unlimited doses of my company,' he reeled off the list cynically, eyes mocking. 'I'd have a proper contract drawn up. Many wives envy their husband's mistresses, my dear. It's not a position you should reject impulsively.'

'Will you just get out of here!' she gasped furiously.

He actually looked amused. 'Get in touch with me when you change your mind,' he invited over his shoulder as he walked through the door and downstairs.

The telephone rang as Lisa stepped from her bath the next morning. She had been up all night since Alex left, unable to sleep or even rest on her bed. There was a hard, hot lump where her heart was supposed to be and she hurt all over. Despite the warmth of her bath, her hands felt icy, her body tortured. When she found it difficult to believe the previous night had ever happened, both her mental and physical state confirmed that it had. The only conclusion she had reached, after hours of suffering, was that she had to get away, yet where could she go without money?

The telephone continued ringing. Fearing it might be Alex she let it ring until she could bear it no longer and picked it up. It was Edward's secretary, he wished to speak to her. Lisa sighed with relief as the woman put her through.

'Good morning, Lisa,' he said cheerfully. 'How are you? Romance still going well?'

Knowing he had been following her friendship with Alex with quiet satisfaction, she hesitated then confessed rawly, 'It's over, Edward, such as it was. I shan't be seeing him again.'

Edward laughed, not taking her seriously. 'All lovers have disagreements.'

'No, it's worse than that.' Again she paused. 'He told me, last night, exactly what he thinks of me.'

'Lisa . . .?'

'No, it wasn't complimentary,' she laughed hollowly. 'He called me a few names I won't repeat and told me I was the last woman he'd consider marrying.'

Edward said something under his breath, unusual for a usually mild-mannered man. 'Lisa, dear, I'm sorry. You'll really have to let me speak to him.'

She couldn't bear even to think of it. 'It's sweet of you to offer, Edward, but it wouldn't do any good. Besides, I don't feel I could see him again. What,' she asked hastily, 'did you want to speak to me about?'

'A client,' he said heavily, as if he knew he was being put off. 'She's a widow, late thirties, lives about a hundred miles away. She's marrying a French diplomat and would like to improve her French. She rang and asked if I knew of anyone who could help, who would be prepared to live with her for a month. She can't pay very much but I can personally vouch for her and you'd be very comfortable. I immediately thought of you,' he added, 'but I didn't say anything as I wasn't sure how involved you'd become with Andreas. However,' he suggested quietly, 'in view of what you've just told me, Lisa, it could give you a chance to get away from town for a while and think over your problems at the same time.'

Privately, Lisa thought it might be a godsend. She accepted with what she supposed was indecent haste. 'As long as you won't tell Alex where I am. He may never enquire but I must be sure.'

'I won't,' Edward promised and proceeded to furnish further details regarding her new employment.

Lisa found her new job extremely pleasant. If she hadn't been so torn by the loss of Alex and her love for him, she would have enjoyed it. She took to Helen

Gilby immediately, liking her directness and courageous outlook on life. Like Lisa, she had lost her husband when still in her twenties but while Lisa's marriage could scarcely have been called a marriage at all, Helen's had obviously been very happy.

One evening, towards the end of the month Lisa was to be with her, Helen mentioned Lisa's marriage tentatively. The friendship and respect between the two women, despite the difference in their ages, had grown to the extent that Lisa found she could talk to Helen fairly easily about things she had never been able to discuss with anyone before, apart from Edward. Without revealing the full facts, she confessed that there had been family reasons for her marriage and it had been one of convenience.

Helen listened attentively and while Lisa was conscious of her warm sympathy, she only said, 'I'm sure you will find true happiness the next time.'

Knowing, for her, there wouldn't be a next time, Lisa said huskily, 'After being so happy with your first husband, Helen, don't you feel doubtful about trying again . . .'

Helen smiled gently as Lisa broke off in confusion having suddenly realised what she was saying. 'You don't have to be embarrassed, Lisa, I know what you mean. How could I bear to marry someone else? Once I'd have thought it impossible. Ten years ago, when Peter died, I believed my life was over. Then, when I met Darnell, I realised it was just one phase of it that was over. Peter was the love of my extreme youth, we shared so many of the very young, carefree things which the years never give again, but I came to recognise that Darnell and I share something just as compelling, if in a slightly different way. I still love Peter but he's part of the past. Now there's Darnell and I know Peter would have liked him, he's such a very special person.'

Lisa realised this when he came for the weekend, her last weekend before she returned to London. He was delighted with Helen's prowess in French but, as he pointed out with a teasing twinkle at Lisa, not surprised as he knew Edward well and trusted his judgment implicitly. They talked French at dinner that first evening, for, as Helen laughingly put it, she wanted to show off, and Lisa tried to push Alex from her mind for a while to join in the light-hearted conversation.

She left early on Monday. She would have gone on Saturday as her work there was finished but neither Helen nor Darnell would hear of it. When she left they both kissed her and Helen said warmly that she hoped Lisa would come and stay with them in Paris and that she couldn't thank her enough for all she had done for her.

On the way to London, Lisa at last decided what she was going to do. Most of her days had been filled for a month but her nights had been spent thinking of Alex. She had lain awake countless hours, fretting for him while contrarily reliving the pain of their last meeting. No matter how many times she went over this, recalling his harsh brutality and scornful, disparaging remarks, she knew she wasn't strong enough to cut him out of her life completely.

For a whole month she had thought she could, but seeing Helen and Darnell together during the weekend, had made her suddenly long for even a little of the happiness that was theirs. Living with Alex—if his offer was still open—could never be the same as being married to him but at least she would have the memory of it to treasure, otherwise she would have nothing.

Lisa gazed through the train window blindly. She wouldn't continue living with him after he was married. Being his mistress while he was still single couldn't hurt anyone but themselves, but after he made this other woman his wife, she would leave him and never see him again.

As soon as she arrived at London she took a taxi to Edward's office. He had asked her to call immediately she got back so he could hear how she had got on and assure himself that she was all right. It always made Lisa feel very humble that he usually saw her as quickly as possible. She had known him cancel an important client and excuse himself in the middle of an interview to see her, and he was one of the city's top lawyers.

'Lisa,' he bent to kiss her cheek, looking at her keenly, 'I hope you are well?'

'Well enough,' she replied, aware that, despite Helen's wonderful cooking she had gone very thin and he noticed. 'I've been working, you know.'

He frowned at her obviously forced smile but merely asked her to sit down and rang for coffee. For the next few minutes, while they drank it, they chatted about Helen and Darnell then Lisa stood up and said lightly, 'I won't keep you, Edward. You're a busy man and my bed needs airing.'

He grinned. 'Not even my legal mind can sort out the intricacies of that.'

'I'm sure it's not necessary,' she laughed.

'By the way,' he sobered abruptly as he walked with her towards the door, 'I've had a terrible time with Andreas while you've been away. He's never been off the telephone and my secretary has threatened to leave each time he storms past her in here, demanding your address.'

'I thought he would be out of the country. Anyway,' she smiled gratefully, hoping he didn't notice she was trembling, 'thank you for not giving it to him.'

'It was the hardest promise I've ever had to keep,' Edward said wryly. 'You said you weren't going to see him again but I fear he intends seeing you. I thought I'd better warn you.'

Lisa didn't tell Edward what she was going to do. She wasn't afraid of his disapproval. Whatever his private thoughts were, he would consider her a free agent and keep them to himself, but she had no wish to worry him unduly. If necessary, she would get in touch with him later. Until she saw Alex there wasn't much point in saying anything.

Once home, she opened the windows to the spring air and made some more coffee. She didn't want any more but hoped it would calm her as she carried it to the telephone. She had been startled to learn that Alex was looking for her. It removed any lingering fears that he was through with her but she didn't try and fool herself that it was going to be easy. Even deciding the best way to contact him was difficult. Eventually she dialled his office.

'Oh, hello, Mrs Fielding.' His secretary sounded suddenly breathless as she gave her name and, without waiting for her to state what she wanted, exclaimed, 'I'll put you through to Mr Andreas right away!'

'No, just tell him I'm home and would like to talk to him, please.'

She put the receiver down on what sounded like a gasp of protest but it only registered vaguely. If Alex had really been looking for her, wanted to see her, now it was up to him.

The coffee not being strong enough to steady her nerves, she poured a small measure of brandy and took a quick gulp. It made her feel sick though it could have been the anticipation inside her rather than the brandy. Alex didn't ring back and she was forced to consider he might not, or that his secretary had forgotten or failed to pass on her message.

To pass the time, she found fresh sheets and made up her bed then went to the bathroom to rinse her hands. Catching a glimpse of herself in the mirror above the basin, she paused in dismay. On leaving Helen's she had looked pale but nothing like this. Hastily she washed her face as well as her hands and reached for her compact. Somehow she managed to disguise the paleness of her face and by skilfully arranging her hair over her cheeks hid most of the ravages of her distress, but she couldn't do a thing about the mad hurtling of her heartbeats when she heard the doorbell ring.

Whoever was there had his thumb on it and wasn't taking it off until he got results. As Lisa stared apprehensively into the mirror, she saw how the colour rushing to her face blended, clown-like, with all the rouge she had put on. Struggling against what seemed an acute lack of oxygen, she reached for a tissue and rubbed some of it off.

The doorbell kept on ringing. It couldn't be Alex so soon, she decided, suddenly coming to her senses and rushing to answer it. Probably it was just one of the children who lived in the street having fun. It was Alex, though, as she discovered as soon as she opened the door and found him standing on the other side of it.

CHAPTER SEVEN

SURPRISINGLY, a great coolness came over Lisa as she stared at him. He was dressed in a grey business suit and, as always, she was struck by his inborn air of superb self-confidence. He looked devastatingly attractive for all his hair was slightly ruffled and his collar loosened in the way of a man hurrying. But his black eyes were hooded and remote and when he spoke his voice was clipped to the point of arrogance.

'Where the hell have you been?'

'That was quick!' she countered, her voice so calm that she couldn't quite believe it.

'Lisa!'

His gaze pinned her to the darkness of his eyes and she suddenly realised she wasn't calm so much as numb. 'Out of town,' she murmured. 'Won't you come in . . .?'

'Did you go because you knew I'd be looking for you?' he rasped, pushing past her and slamming the door.

'Looking for me?' she murmured vaguely, turning automatically towards the lounge.

Catching her roughly by the shoulders, he swung her around. 'Don't walk away from me,' he grated. 'Answer my question! Didn't you guess I'd be looking for you?'

His conceit amazed her but she wouldn't lie to him. 'When you left here, the last time, you hardly gave me the impression that you would be.'

His quick anger appeared to leave him though his eyes were still hard. 'I realise you wouldn't be expecting me to, but I've been worried.'

Demented, was more the word Edward had used, but he must have been mistaken. Alex's cold demeanour scarcely betrayed any real concern. 'Why were you— worried?' she asked haltingly.

114

'Do I really have to explain?' he snapped impatiently, 'You were obviously upset by what I said to you and when you disappeared I felt responsible. In your state of mind, you might have done something foolish.'

'You didn't like feeling guilty?'

Stung by her sharp tone, he lashed back. 'I'm not totally without compassion, even for those who don't deserve it.'

'The last thing I want from you is pity,' she flared, realising they were quarrelling but when it came to it, finding it easier to utter the angry words that sprang to her lips than to confess what she had really wanted to see him about.

His eyes suddenly narrowed in a face which she saw, like her own, was thinner. She could almost see him doing some swift rethinking. 'You sent for me, there must be something?'

'Yes . . .' Strange how calm she felt over taking such a momentous step which would change her whole life. 'You, made me an offer . . .'

The change in him was remarkable. His black eyes leapt, he didn't try to hide the flames in them as his voice thickened. 'I said I still wanted you as my mistress. You refused, but now, do I take it you have changed your mind?'

'Yes.' She didn't waver but she had to lower her eyes before the triumph in his. She couldn't escape it in his voice, though, as he pulled her swiftly into his arms.

'Lisa.' His arms were like steel, binding her to him but the hand that forced her to look at him was warm and caressing. 'I knew you would come to your senses, my darling. I promise you won't regret it.'

Exultantly he bent his head to claim her mouth, kissing her with exquisite gentleness, his tongue teasing her lips apart. They still had things to talk about but she was filled with such a weakness that she immediately forgot everything but the fact that Alex was holding her again, after so many long weeks apart.

Slowly she began to respond to the passionate persuasiveness of his mouth until such a surge of desire consumed her that she drew sharply back.

Her swift withdrawal didn't bother him as it used to do. Since she had given in to him, he was willing to humour her. It wouldn't be long before she was with him night and day and he could wait. Reading the burning, primitive hunger in his eyes, the message they so clearly conveyed, Lisa began to tremble.

'We will fly straight to Athens,' he said.

'Your own country?'

He laughed, she could feel his spirits soaring. 'I can't think of another place I'd rather be when I possess you. I promised myself it would be like this, the first time I saw you. Other men may have had you but no one but me will ever have you again. I swear I'll kill any other man you even glance at.'

She flushed, her heart racing, but was able to say firmly, 'Before I agree to go anywhere, Alex, you must agree to one or two things.'

'Such as?' he asked.

She hated the cynical twist to his mouth, knowing he was wondering how good a settlement she would try and get out of him. Drawing a deep breath, she said, 'I will be your mistress, Alex, but I won't live with you. I want to keep my own house, and when we are abroad, if it's for any length of time, I'll live in either a rented apartment or a hotel.'

'You're crazy.' He frowned, clearly uncertain whether to take her seriously. 'I want you with me all the time, to find you in my bed when I wake up in the mornings. I'll want to make love to you in the mornings, Lisa, as well as other hours of the day. How do you think we are going to manage that if we aren't living together?'

The colour in her cheeks deepened but she went on adamantly. 'I won't sell my house for the minute you take a wife I won't see you again.'

For a moment he looked quite thunderstruck then he

rasped, 'Why, in God's name, won't you see me again? What difference is my marriage going to make?'

She looked at him bitterly. Was he completely insensitive? 'All the difference in the world,' she said tensely. 'While you are single, whatever relationship we share, we can't hurt anyone but ourselves. But I refuse to help you to be an unfaithful husband.'

Anger tautened his features harshly. 'Hadn't you better think about what you are saying? How will my marriage alter your feelings for me? Looking at it from your angle, will you be able to simply walk away from me, pretend I never happened? Once we become lovers, do you really believe you will be able to forget me?'

'That's not the point,' she argued despairingly. 'Despite my experience with Philip, or perhaps because of it, I happen to believe that marriage should be a sacred undertaking . . .'

'It took you long enough to find out.'

In the light of what he believed of her, he would consider himself justified in making such a statement. Lisa winced but wouldn't be deflected from what she wanted to say. 'Another thing, I refuse to accept any gifts of money, jewellery or clothing from you. While I am with you, you may keep me but, otherwise, nothing else.'

'And what if I don't agree?' he asked curtly.

'Then it's all off,' she declared tautly. He was furious, she could see, but he was also watching her cautiously, as if judging the best line to take with her. 'I won't go one yard with you, Alex,' she added, 'unless you do.'

'I could make you go with me regardless,' he threatened. 'I'm an extremely wealthy man, Lisa. I have ways and means not available to most people.'

'I realise the power you have,' she retorted quietly, 'and you can use it if you don't mind my hating you, but hate isn't much fun in bed, Alex.'

A muscle jerked in his strong throat. 'You should know as you've been through it.' His eyes smouldered with a hint of something she didn't understand, then he gave in. 'Very well, I agree, though if I had any sense I would leave this minute, and alone. Unfortunately I can't,' he groaned, catching hold of her again and muttering against her lips, 'You're in my blood, as you already know. I've tried for weeks to get you out and there's only one way left. As for my marriage to Letha, we shall see. I somehow doubt that after belonging to me, you'll be able to leave me when the time comes.'

'I will,' she said stubbornly.

'I wouldn't bet on it, my darling,' he replied arrogantly. 'You returned to me of your own free will, remember, and you've already confessed that you love me. Or,' he paused viciously, 'were those just empty words which you've whispered to every fool who ever held you in his arms?'

'Certainly I was a fool to imagine I loved you,' she cried bitterly. 'Like you, I'm trapped by feelings much less admirable, which I don't think we need discuss.'

He almost threw her away from him in a gesture which was becoming too painfully familiar. 'Go and pack,' he snarled, 'before I lose my temper completely, then maybe we shall both be sorry.

'I can't leave immediately!' she gasped.

'Why not?' he snapped. 'You have your passport, there's nothing to keep you . . .'

'The electricity,' she mumbled, searching for any excuse that might give her a little more time.

'Lisa,' he remonstrated, drawing her roughly back into his arms. 'Do you wish to begin living with me here? I may appear to be relatively calm but inside I'm about eaten up with desire for you. I have one or two things I'd rather get out of the way first, but the main reason why I'm not upstairs with you, right now, is that I'd rather begin our life together in Greece.'

'Oh, Alex,' she breathed, frightened by the sudden rawness of his voice yet unable to stop herself from responding to it. She knew he wouldn't allow her to escape from him at this late stage, and she didn't want to. She couldn't talk to him any more about love but her heart was still full of it. It weakened any defence she had against him but she couldn't get rid of a certain apprehension regarding the step she was taking.

As if aware of her nervousness, Alex held her tighter and said gently, 'Trust me, my darling, try not to worry. Concentrate on our future, how much I want you, how much I hope you want me.'

'I do,' she whispered, not able to fight her overwhelming feelings any longer. Putting her arms around him slowly, she could feel the need in the strong, hard body pressing against her own. She sighed, resting her head on his broad chest. 'I do want you, Alex, all this past month, I've missed you and longed for you so.'

'Just wait until tonight,' he promised thickly. 'You won't have any regrets then.'

They landed in Athens several hours later, having travelled by private jet from London. Lisa wasn't surprised to discover Alex used his own planes and, in a way, she was relieved that he had arranged for several members of his staff to travel with them. Her own presence must have been noted with some speculation but, with Alex around, no one obviously dared do more than speculate, not even among themselves. Those who were with them were mostly English and American but Alex kept them so occupied with business that they barely got a chance to speak to her.

In Athens, they all parted company, the staff going straight to his headquarters, where he arranged to see them later, while he and Lisa were driven to his apartment.

As their chauffeur-driven limousine drew up in the forecourt outside it, Lisa immediately recognised it and exclaimed angrily, 'You promised I would stay in a hotel.'

'Don't worry, darling,' he smiled benignly, 'I haven't

forgotten what I agreed to but there hasn't been time to make the necessary arrangements. I've been getting some urgent business out of the way in order to leave myself free for the next few weeks. In any case it wouldn't be worthwhile booking you into a hotel as, tomorrow, we shall be going away.' His eyes glowed into her doubtful face. 'This evening we shall discuss everything.'

Lisa wasn't sure what to think but as she was learning how fruitless it was to defy Alex openly, she didn't say anything more. Perhaps his apartment might be the best for tonight, she thought, but even as she tried to reassure herself, the sick feeling returned to her stomach.

The apartment, when Alex opened the door, was strangely silent. 'Where is everyone?' she asked uncertainly.

'If you mean the servants, they're on the island.' He shrugged. 'There's good room service, though, so you don't have anything to worry about.'

'The island?' Lisa was briefly diverted. 'Are you talking about Enos?'

'No.' He picked up her luggage and carried it to his bedroom, indicating for her to follow. 'I haven't done anything about Enos yet. I thought I'd mentioned it, I live on another island.'

Had he told her about it? 'You probably did—in fact,' she frowned, trying to remember, 'didn't you say you were fond of it?'

'Very.'

Though puzzled by his terse tones, the thought of an island filled her with pleasure and she asked eagerly, 'Is this where you are taking me tomorrow?'

'I don't think so.'

Such an honour would be reserved for his wife! She forced a smile to hide her sudden pain, knowing it wouldn't be the last time a similar remark of his would hurt her. And this was a situation which she had, after all, gone into with her eyes wide open.

'Darling!' Alex put her cases down by the bed and gathered her close. 'If you would like to stay on an island there are plenty to choose from. I know of at least three I could borrow from friends.'

Who would know exactly why he wanted one ... 'Let's wait,' she said quickly. 'Didn't you say you had to go out again?'

'I wish I hadn't to,' he sighed, passion prowling in his eyes as he bent his head and his lips moved gently on hers. 'When I return though, there will be no more interruptions.'

The hurt inside her, the strangeness of her surroundings, they all vanished beneath the warmth of his mouth. The heat from it spread through her and she melted into him, feeling only an incredible wave of pleasure.

Only then did he ease the pressure he was exerting on her slightly. 'You're beautiful,' he said huskily, his heart thudding under his shirt so she could actually feel it. 'Some day I'm going to dress you in silks and satins, drape you with furs and diamonds, but I doubt if they will make you any lovelier than you are now.'

He allowed her no time to protest but drew her urgently against him again, crushing his mouth ruthlessly against hers. Lisa closed her eyes, every inch of her aware of his towering height, the steely strength of his sinews, the effect of his body on hers. Almost overwhelmed by it, she put her arms around his neck and clung to him, returning his kisses blindly.

He picked her up then fell beside her on the huge bed. The look in his eyes made her tremble as he unbuttoned her blouse and bared her breasts. His expression changed slightly as his glance wandered further over her and he saw how thin she had become.

'Little fool,' he said gruffly, 'what's been happening to you? You must have lost pounds.'

'I've been teaching a lady French,' she said, 'nothing else.'

'So that's why I couldn't find you.' His eyes sharpened with sudden interest. 'You're far too thin.' His hand pressed the flatness of her stomach. 'You will have to put weight on again as you're going to need all your strength, my darling. Once I take you, I'm never going to be satisfied.'

She smiled at him, only half aware of what he was saying, having been too busy studying the strong, sensuous lines of his face. Shyly experimenting, she caressed his cheek with exploratory fingers then rubbed her thumb provocatively over his lower lips.

His breathing quickened. Then he was on top of her, his weight pushing her into the mattress, his kisses growing deeper and more demanding. Her flesh felt as if on fire as his hands roamed over her, until she longed for his total possession.

Then, just as suddenly, he rolled off her and stood up. She heard him cursing under his breath even before she opened dazed eyes and found him glancing at his watch.

'Dammit!' he rasped. 'I'll have to go, they'll be waiting . . .'

'Couldn't you ring them,' she groaned, unable to return to reality immediately and only aware that she didn't want him to leave her.

'What would I say?' The flush on his cheeks faded but his fingers shook so much he had a struggle to fasten his shirt, which seemed to make him angry. 'That my mistress couldn't wait?'

Lisa lay still where he had left her, beginning to shiver. Only dimly did she hear his curt assurance that he would be no more than an hour or two, before the outer door slammed. Her eyes filled with tears as his last remark churned around and around in her head. It might have been trapped there, and made of iron spikes, it caused her so much pain.

There was no sense in asking herself any more questions, not when she knew all the answers. She was only here to satisfy Alex's physical needs. He wanted to make love to her and, loving him as she did, she was powerless to resist him. The knowledge wasn't new but filled her with bitter-sweet emotion. Barely nine hours ago she had decided to accept from him whatever he offered, on whatever terms, believing she couldn't live apart from him. Yet now they were together, she realised that would never be enough. To love without being loved in return, to have to learn to be regarded as someone to be made use of. Of having to bear the tolerant contempt of Alex's friends, just as she'd had to bear that of Philip's. Without thinking, she had incredulously put her head in the same noose again. She had insisted on a few foolish conditions imagining they would make everything all right. She hadn't had the sense to see the pitfalls, how being Alex's mistress, would mean constantly swinging between joy and misery, hope and despair.

With an audible sob, Lisa suddenly wrenched herself off the bed to her feet. It might not yet be too late to reverse the misguided decision she had made. Blindly she tidied herself up as she gazed distractedly about her. Where was the telephone? Not by Alex's bed. Bitterly her thoughts ran on ... Naturally he wouldn't risk being disturbed the nights he spent here with his other mistresses!

Rushing through the hall, she found one in the study. Hastily, though her fingers felt all thumbs, she dialled the airport. She almost laughed hysterically as she repeated the same procedure as she had done the last time she had been here but managed to control the choking sounds in her throat. If she was to escape Alex a second time, she knew she must keep a clear head.

When she was told there wasn't a seat available on the next flight to London, her heart sank. Surely, on a weekday, there must be? On a desperate impulse, she gambled on the only thing she could think of. 'I'm a friend of Mr Andreas,' she said.

There was a pause during which she held her breath. 'Mr Alexander Andreas?' a more halting voice asked.

'Yes.'

The booking clerk muttered something in Greek, then, in hasty English, 'One moment, please.'

There was a cancellation. Lisa was too relieved to demand an explanation as to why there hadn't been until she mentioned Alex's name. The clerk didn't offer one and it might have been a coincidence. She merely requested that Lisa should be at the airport as soon as possible as the flight would be leaving within the next two hours.

Lisa was in a taxi, speeding towards the airport within a few minutes. Having done it before made it easier but she had to strive to steady her jumping nerves. She had left her luggage behind, Alex could destroy it for all she cared. She had also left a note saying she had gone for a walk, which she hoped might stop him searching for her immediately. He would be furious when he discovered she had returned to London but she prayed he would let her go this time.

Despite refusing to consider that Alex might catch up with her. Lisa's whole body was damp with perspiration by the time she checked in and joined the crowds in the departure lounge. She tried to merge where they were thickest, where she might be unnoticed. She couldn't imagine, even if Alex finished his business quickly, that he would come looking for her here. More likely, when he found her note, he would be hunting the streets around his apartment, and long before he discovered where she really was, she would be gone.

For all this, she did her best to remain as inconspicuous as possible until her flight was called. It filled her with despair, afterwards, to realise that if she hadn't been so dumb and had chosen a quiet corner to hide in, she might have avoided the subsequent publicity.

That she didn't even notice Alex approaching was another omission she levelled against her intelligence.

She wasn't aware of him until a hand descended on her shoulder and the shock which ran through her told her immediately whose hand it was even before she swung around and looked at him.

His impaling power was monstrous, she could only gasp his name. 'Alex!'

His black eyes scorched her out of a furious face. 'At least you still remember my name.'

'H—how did you find me?' she stammered.

'One or two educated guesses plus a little help,' he retorted, without disclosing where the help had come from. But he wasn't disposed to talk or linger as, releasing her shoulder, he grabbed an arm and began dragging her through the interested crowd.

To Lisa's apprehensive, 'Where are we going?' he replied between his teeth, 'Home.'

Gathering up the scattered remnants of her courage, she was just about to try and dig her heels in when she noticed the photographers bearing down on them triumphantly.

'What did you expect?' Alex gritted, glancing balefully at her aghast face. 'Don't complain about them, you little tramp, when you play games specially designed to attract them.'

'I don't!' she breathed. 'I was only waiting for a plane. I want to go home, Alex, but to London. Didn't you get my note? I know I just said I was going for a walk but you must have realised that everything between us is over.'

'Lovers' tiff, Mr Andreas?' shouted a grinning photographer, blinding them with repeated flashes while newsmen scribbled.

'We all have them,' Alex retorted dismissively.

'How long have you and Mr Andreas been living together, Mrs Fielding?' another asked, while the crowd gasped and surged forward.

Lisa thought she was going to faint. 'I—we aren't,' she began . . .

'How long have you been his mistress?' yelled a voice from a London paper.

As Lisa shrank against him, Alex turned on the media formidably. 'You can retract that, gentlemen, as soon as you like. Mrs Fielding and I are getting married. She's my fiancée.'

There was a startled silence. One or two of the newsmen actually looked sheepish. There were more gasps from the people about them and a whole new buzz of excited conversation.

'When did Mrs Fielding agree to marry you, Mr Andreas?' One of the press stepped in front of him as he tried to shield Lisa's stunned face and draw her away.

'Just recently,' he replied coolly. 'I've been trying to persuade her for weeks.'

'And the wedding?'

'That's our business. I imagine you will know soon enough,' he retorted drily. 'Now I'd be much obliged if you'd take yourselves off and leave us alone.'

No one appeared ready to argue with the steely expression on Alex Andreas's face. Lisa, hanging on to his arm tightly, saw them obeying him through a thickening haze.

'A scoop!' one shouted jubilantly.

Feeling sick and faint, she choked, 'They're like vultures!'

'Only doing their job, darling.'

Lisa's eyes widened as she realised they still had an audience of tourists and other travellers and that Alex was still acting the part of a lovingly tolerant fiancé.

As he turned her firmly away from them, she wondered if any of them noticed his arm wasn't nearly as gentle as his voice. 'I can manage by myself,' she murmured painfully, but when he abruptly let go of her, she stumbled so badly that he had to grab hold of her again. 'I'm sorry,' she whispered, head drooping.

'I suggest you show it by shutting up,' he said grimly. 'Let's get out of here.'

'I have to go back to London,' she gabbled, feeling ill.

'You will, eventually. With me.'

He sounded so adamant that she couldn't fight him any more, even if she'd had the strength. A car was waiting to drive them swiftly from the airport. She sat tensely in the back of it beside Alex. By running away she had made everything a thousand times worse. It hadn't helped anything. Alex had felt forced to tell the press they were about to be married. It would be in all the papers tomorrow and there would have to be a further announcement cancelling their supposed engagement. And it would have to be done almost immediately, to save embarrassment. She felt cold even though the evening was still warm, and was unable to think of a thing to say.

Back at the apartment, Alex dismissed the driver and they went inside. The strained silence between them was telling on Lisa badly. In the lounge she could only stare at Alex with eyes which seemed to be haunted.

He had followed closely, as if he didn't intend letting her out of his sight. 'How did you discover that I'd gone and where I was?' she asked weakly, rather than start straight in with what was uppermost on her mind. 'You haven't any servants here to let you know, as they did last time.'

'I told you, I had a little help,' he snapped. 'Let that suffice.'

Lisa swallowed and her throat hurt. If Alex was still furious, hadn't he the right to be? He had pursued her but she had come with him of her own free will. He had certainly never led her to believe he would ever marry her. She took a deep breath and plunged—it would only get worse, the longer she hesitated. 'Why did you tell the press we were engaged?'

His eyes glittered and his voice had the bite of steel in it as he said enigmatically, 'You didn't hesitate to use my name when it suited you, did you? So you'd better get used to the idea of adopting it more or less permanently. We shall be married in a day or two, as soon as it can be arranged.'

Her head was swimming, she could only see blazing black eyes and a tight mouth. She saw no sign of the tenderness he had shown her earlier in the evening. 'Alex!' She had to make him understand that she couldn't marry him. 'I was returning to London because I suddenly realised I'd made a terrible mistake. It wasn't your fault that I suddenly knew I couldn't stay here, or anywhere, and live with you, but I honestly didn't mean to embarrass you as I did. I think we should forget the whole thing and I'll go home tomorrow.'

'No you won't!' he sounded incensed. 'You were eager enough to marry me a month ago. You may have trapped me into it at the airport, but I find I'm quite willing to be married to you, if this is what you want, until I tire of you. You decided not to be my mistress but you might wish to God you had been before I'm through with you. As my mistress, you could have had almost anything you asked for. You knew that and rejected it, but you won't be able to reject your lot as my wife. I will have an agreement drawn up immediately and you will sign it, whether it suits you or not.'

'Alex! You have to be sensible,' she gulped, feeling ready to weep, she was so frightened. 'You don't want to marry me . . .'

'I want you,' he retorted icily, 'and if you won't live with me it's the only way.'

'And, later, you'll divorce me.' Her face flamed. 'W-what if there are children?'

'They will stay with me.'

'No,' she shook her head distractedly, 'I love children—I could never bear to leave my own. It would never work out.'

'Not as you would like it to, perhaps, but that's

something you must learn to accept.' His mouth twisted contemptuously. 'You got us into this and if I have little choice, neither have you. I certainly won't have the world laughing at me by breaking off our engagement and letting them believe you turned me down. But I can assure you, you won't find me as easy to twist around your little finger, as you did Philip Fielding.'

'It wasn't like that with Philip and me,' she protested, only to be rudely interrupted.

'I'm not interested in how it was!' he shouted, his face filled with the rage he could no longer control. 'Don't you know better than to try and push your luck? I warn you, Lisa, I'll only take so much.'

She gasped at the hatred in his eyes while her throat ached with the tears she couldn't shed. 'We'll only hurt each other, Alex.' She made one last plea. 'How can we ever hope to find happiness . . .?'

'Who said anything about happiness?' he said cruelly. 'You know what I'm marrying you for and it's not that.'

Silently she stared at him, at the harsh, uncompromising lines of his face as he stared back. 'All right,' she whispered raggedly. 'You win.'

'And you can stop looking like an ill-treated child,' he snapped, swinging abruptly from her to pace the floor. 'I'll ring for Paul and a housekeeper, they should lend an air of respectability for a few nights. You remember Paul, my assistant, don't you? Tomorrow I shall see my solicitors and work out a marriage contract, and immediately after we are married we shall fly to the island.'

He couldn't have discussed a business proposition with less emotion and as he swung back to her, his eyes were hard. 'How does that sound?'

She looked at him unhappily. 'The only thing I like the sound of is your island.'

'Poor Lisa,' he mocked, going to the telephone and

barking a few orders into the receiver. Then, after redialling, he ordered dinner.

He spoke in Greek but his order was so lengthy that Lisa wondered who was going to eat it. Coming back to her again, as if he guessed what she was thinking, he coolly raised her chin and kissed her. 'I told you before, you need fattening up. Do you wish me to repeat the reasons?'

Lisa flushed and tried to find some composure. She sensed it was no use talking to him in his present mood. She didn't really believe it would do any good trying to talk him out of marrying her whatever kind of a mood he was in, but at the moment she would certainly be wasting her breath.

'Lost your tongue?' he jeered, releasing her chin but letting his hands slide to her shoulders.

'No.' She wished he would let her go. His hands hurt, she suspected intentionally, but they also sent shafts of disturbing feeling shooting through her.

'I hope,' his eyes narrowed, 'you aren't planning to beg Paul's assistance?'

'I shouldn't dream of involving Paul,' she retorted. 'Before he arrives though, I'd like to ask what you intend doing about this other woman whom you intended making your bride? I know what it feels like to be rejected.' She lowered thick lashes so he couldn't read what was in her eyes. 'I wouldn't wish to feel responsible for hurting anyone.'

'There was nothing arranged.' Se shrugged. 'Which is probably just as well.'

'There must have been an understanding?' She frowned, trying to remember clearly what he had told her.

'Not even that, though her father had approached me,' he revealed stiffly. 'You don't have to worry about Letha, Lisa, she will soon find someone else.'

'She will probably be better off with someone else,' Lisa said sharply. 'You can't love her, otherwise you wouldn't be marrying me.'

His mouth tightened. 'In Greece, family pride and esteem is regarded as more important than some improbable emotion.'

'I'm not even getting that,' she said rawly.

'Complaining already, are you?' he taunted. 'Perhaps I should give you something to really complain about?'

Before she could move, he crushed his lips over hers and savaged her mouth. His arms, just as ruthless, tightened relentlessly as he pulled her against him. Lisa's fingers tensed on his shoulders but she didn't struggle. He was still angry but she could sense it filtering away as his passion took over. His heart began thudding against her own and sweat broke out on his skin as his body immediately hardened. Suddenly she lost all desire to fight him. Feeling only an overwhelming need to comfort him, her arms curved about his neck and she began kissing him back slowly.

CHAPTER EIGHT

WHEN tears started squeezing through her tightly closed eyelids, Lisa was as startled as the man holding her. She felt him pause in his ravaging punishment of her mouth then slowly raise his head to look at her.

'Lisa?' His fingers gently touched her wet cheeks then he stiffened. 'You don't have to be frightened that I'll insist on sleeeping with you, tonight.'

She'd had a long day, which might partly account for her tears, but she no longer had any intention of denying him. 'I'm not frightened,' she began . . .

'Then you're tired, and I don't want an exhausted woman in my arms,' he cut in curtly. He still held her in an iron grip but his passion was under control again. 'I can wait now until after the wedding, as long as you don't try and cheat me then. If you do, don't expect any mercy.'

'I've never tried to cheat you,' she said, suddenly hurt.

'If you have another name for it,' he snapped, 'I haven't. You've tantalised me for weeks, holding yourself just out of reach. You promised to be my mistress and changed your mind. You're not even sure about marriage, only you know, with your reputation, you may never get another chance. I must be the biggest fool on earth to be even thinking of marrying you.'

'You don't have to,' she retorted, suddenly weary of their continual wrangling. 'At least you can't accuse me of being dishonest about this. I can leave this very minute and you needn't ever see me again.'

'You could, and I wish I had the strength to let you,' he said savagely. 'It's got to be marriage. I've tried every other way to get you out of my system and it might be a big price to pay, but pay it I will. You can talk about leaving me when I tire of you.'

Three days later they were married quietly in a small church, so tucked away in a labyrinth of side-streets in Athens that Lisa felt less like a bride than a criminal.

She was wearing a new outfit, a silky blue dress and matching jacket, but it wasn't one she had bought herself. Alex had confiscated all her clothes and supplied her with a whole new wardrobe. He had demanded her measurements and sent them to one of the best dress shops in the city. When she had protested, he had snapped that he wouldn't allow her to continue wearing any clothing bought for her by Philip Fielding.

He had given her an engagement ring which again she wasn't allowed to choose, and disposed of Philip's wedding ring. After this he had relaxed all but his guard over her, for all she had promised she wouldn't run away again. When he wasn't with her, Paul had looked after her, never letting her out of his sight. What reason Alex had given Paul for this, Lisa wasn't sure, and she didn't ask Paul, for all she caught him gazing at her curiously several times.

She hadn't seen a lot of Alex during the past three days. He had been busy and when he was with her, he alternated so frequently between passion and disdain that the state of her nerves grew steadily worse. He could be warm and tender one moment, brutally hurtful the next. Sometimes there was no reasoning with him, he demanded and commanded and this frightened her when she thought of their wedding night. His growing impatience disconcerted her even while she somehow managed to stay calm and hide it.

She had wondered, on deciding to become his mistress, if he would be vexed or pleased when he discovered she was a virgin, and though the situation had altered, she was still wondering. Two days ago, she had tried to tell him but when, as on all the other occasions, he wouldn't listen, she had resolved to wait and let him find out for himself.

It was only her love for him, she realised, that had kept her going over the previous days, a love that she hoped would stand her in good stead in the months ahead. She wasn't of such an angelic disposition that she didn't feel like retaliating when she had clothes, orders, compliments and insults thrown at her indiscriminately. Secretly she had arrived at the conclusion that Alex, despite being a sophisticated, international figure, was, underneath it all, as savagely untamed as some of his primitive ancestors. It had flashed through her mind before, but during the days immediately preceding their wedding, she became convinced of it.

Standing beside him, repeating her marriage vows, and afterwards, as they flew out from Athens in one of Alex's twin engined Bell helicopters, she couldn't help wondering what the future held for her. There had been no one at their wedding apart from Paul and the surprising number of priests who had officiated. Alex had been formidably silent throughout with only his burning eyes and compressed mouth betraying he wasn't as calm as he appeared to be. Whether the peculiar smouldering in the black depth of his pupils had denoted anger or regret, Lisa couldn't tell. Probably both, she decided unhappily.

She was still wearing her blue suit, her bridal bouquet a bunch of white flowers, still clutched in her hands. Alex and she had almost quarrelled over the flowers when she had asked for white ones and he'd been unable to hide his scorn.

'Wishful thinking won't change what you are,' he had grated, and she had turned away from him, trying to hide her distress. She hadn't asked for a white dress, surely a few flowers of that colour needn't offend him?

The smell of the flowers was sickly now, in the

confined space, and suddenly she threw them on the seat behind her. From where he was sitting, Alex turned his head to glance at her mockingly and she was thankful Paul couldn't see him from where he was piloting the helicopter.

A long time later, or so it seemed to Lisa, they landed on an island which she saw was much larger than Enos but just as isolated. 'Welcome to Sanara,' Alex shouted, above the noise of the engine.

There was a small group of people waiting near the landing pad and a short distance away she could see a sprawling white house. It was near the sea, she caught a glimpse of green grounds, patios and swimming pools before Alex dropped to the ground and lifted her down. She got the impression of unstinted luxury yet in some ways it reminded her of Enos for, beyond the gardens the land looked as wild and uncultivated.

As Alex held her, until she was steady on her feet, the crowd, obviously servants from the villa, surged forward, curious to see their master's new wife. They were greeted with cheers while the men bowed as Alex introduced her and the women curtsied. Lisa thanked them for their good wishes shyly, her pale cheeks colouring prettily when one of the women asked her something and she referred to Alex for the first time as her husband. Most of them spoke a little English but Lisa made up her mind to begin learning Greek immediately.

Alex had a word with Paul who was leaving again as soon as he checked the helicopter. Then he spoke in a low voice to one of the older women whom he had introduced as the housekeeper. After this, while the men picked picked up their luggage, they started towards the house, the other women following, chattering excitedly.

Alex took Lisa's arm. 'Filana tells me that my aunt is waiting inside.'

'Your—aunt?' He hadn't mentioned that anyone

would be here besides themselves and she felt her nerves tighten. 'You didn't say.'

He ignored the unconscious reproach in her voice. 'Madeline Demetris, my father's sister, is the only aunt I have. She often visits but the house is large enough to accommodate her without interfering with our privacy.'

'That's not what I'm worrying about.' Lisa glanced up at him anxiously. 'Your aunt may not like me. If she expected you to marry one of your own countrywomen, it won't be surprising if she's upset.'

'Lisa! Stop inventing problems where none exist,' he reproved drily. 'It really makes little difference whether she likes you or not, but, as she is here, I hope you will do your best to be pleasant to her.'

Lisa flushed indignantly. 'I'm usually pleasant to people but that wasn't the point I was trying to make.'

'Never mind,' he said softly and, with what she considered, a maddening lack of consistency. 'Madeline's opinion of you is of no importance. Tonight is important, though, and I don't want you to have anything but me on your mind.'

His only concern for her feelings was the way they might react on him if his aunt did anything to depress her. She felt like slapping him as he looked down on her, the satisfaction of ownership almost stamped on his dark face. He really did consider he owned her. It was in his eyes, the complacent firmness of his mouth, in every proprietary line of his tall, lean body. Lisa blinked and drew her breath in sharply.

They entered a cool, white vestibule then a spacious entrance hall through wide doorways. Lisa glanced quickly around, rather startled by the sheer size of everything. Large reception rooms flanked the hall with long passages leading off to the bedrooms and domestic offices. What she could see of it was well but sparsely furnished. Her mother would have said it needed a woman's touch.

It was the woman coming out of the main lounge,

however, who claimed Lisa's more immediate attention. She was tall for a woman and Lisa wouldn't have liked to have tried to guess her age. Her face was lined but she walked very straight, with the kind of dignified bearing which somehow defies age.

She kissed Alex with disapproving formality before turning to Lisa, her eyes curiously blank. 'So you are my nephew's bride.'

Mutely, Lisa submitted to the cool lips brushing her cheek but tensed when Madame addressed Alex again. 'I can't understand why you choose to get married so suddenly and secretly and, above all, to Philip Fielding's widow?'

Lisa felt shocked, even while she tried to tell herself there could be nothing personal in Madame's remark. She heard Alex replying coolly, 'Once I make up my mind, Madeline, you know I never prevaricate. And I had no desire to endure the fuss of a big wedding.'

'Hadn't you any say in the matter?' Madame asked Lisa drily.

'Very little,' Alex answered for her. 'Now,' he said firmly, 'if you will excuse us, Madeline, I will show Lisa to our room. She will want to freshen up before dinner.'

'Very well, but come back and talk to me, Alex,' his aunt called after him presumptuously.

If Lisa hadn't felt so disturbed she might have smiled. It was easy to see which side of the family Alex got his arrogance from. Yet she found she couldn't dislike Madame Demetris. At least one would always know where one stood with her. As for the tone of voice she had used when she had referred to her being Philip's widow, Lisa decided, for Alex's sake, to do her best to forget it.

Their luggage had already been taken to a large suite at the end of the main corridor. To reach it they climbed a low flight of stairs which raised it to well above ground level, giving wonderful views out over the gardens and sea while making it impossible for anyone to see in.

A maid was just finishing unpacking Lisa's clothes and Alex dismissed her. The girl curtsied and smiled and replied in Greek as she went out.

'I must learn Greek as soon as possible,' Lisa said.

'How many languages do you speak?' Alex asked casually, tugging off his tie.

'Four besides my own,' she smiled wryly, 'I was good at them at school. Unfortunately I never learned yours.'

'There are other things I'm going to teach you first.' He grinned tigerishly, suddenly reaching for her, his mouth descending on hers the moment she was in his arms.

As the searing impact of his kiss shot through her, Lisa was dazed by a surge of desire that took her by surprise. Her response was so instantaneous and complete that she was tempted to cling to him passionately and beg him to take her straight to bed. Her heart was beating so fast it was sending every pulse in her body into a mad frenzy. She wanted him and suspected he knew it.

Not ready yet to accept such a lack of inhibition in herself, with her last sane thought she grasped his shoulders, intent on pushing him away before the heat of his mouth dissolved the last of her resistance.

'Please,' she whispered against his lips, 'not now!'

'I could take you now.' His breathing was heavy as he stared down into her hot face. As she raised clouded blue eyes, he muttered, 'I want you more than I ever wanted any other woman and I don't know how patient I'll be able to be, but I don't want to have to get up and dressed and go in to dinner afterwards, I doubt if I could eat any, once I've had a taste of you. So,' his mouth twisted ruefully, 'if we aren't to disappoint Madeline and the crowd of well-wishers whom I suspect are going to turn up, I'll have to grant you a short reprieve. As long as you aren't thinking of it as a stay of execution.'

Silently Lisa shook her head and managed to smile at him gratefully. He was, after all, her husband, and she loved him. He wanted her badly, she would have had to be blind not to have seen the agony of need in his eyes, and she shared his feelings. But she also wanted to give herself to him for the comfort he was going to derive from their union. She wasn't a sadist, able to enjoy extending his unappeased hunger. It only made her feel guilty now, to be denying him anything.

'You do want me,' he demanded, as if her silent confirmation wasn't enough.

'Of course I do!' Her voice was low and husky, trembling slightly like the hands she raised to caress his face. 'Oh, Alex, you know how I feel about you. Whatever else is missing from our relationship, it's not that.'

'It doesn't matter about anything else,' he said roughly, tightening his hold of her then relaxing it again with a muttered curse. 'If I kiss you again we're never going to get out of here. We'd better shower and dress.'

Twenty minutes later, exactly, Lisa was ready. The warm water and her own growing elation, which somehow she wasn't able to suppress, had taken a lot of the tension out of her, making her feel ready to face a thousand aunts! She had even convinced herself that if she persevered and was a dutiful wife, Alex might easily come to love her as she loved him. He hadn't mentioned divorce again, which seemed to prove it had only occupied him briefly. Shoving any lingering doubts from her mind, she saw a wonderful future stretching before her with Alex always by her side, along with several engaging sons and daughters. Even thinking of it brought a radiant glow to her face which stopped her husband in his tracks as he came from his dressing-room.

He took in the picture she made, the white dress with its gold belt making nothing of her narrow waist, the golden hair, which was so pale in places as to be no colour at all, lying in a thick, gleaming swathe over her shoulders. She wore no make-up, apart from a little mascara and lip gloss and her skin was perfect. And he thought her eyes a more vivid blue than any sky he had yet seen over the island.

He came slowly towards her, his glance lingering over her face, her long, slender neck, the shadowed cleft between her taut breasts. 'Did you have to make yourself so beautiful?' he asked unsteadily, his breath shuddering. 'I had decided to enjoy my dinner.'

'Poor Alex,' she laughed, suddenly daring to tease, 'I must think of some way of compensating you.'

'You'd better,' he growled, the kiss he crushed on her lips leaving her in no doubt as to what he was thinking of as he took her reluctantly back to the lounge.

Throughout dinner, Lisa was aware of Madeline's eyes resting on her frequently and she couldn't be sure whether she had gained a friend or made an enemy. Madeline monopolised the conversation, which was mostly about people Lisa didn't know. The odd times she spoke to Lisa, her voice was stilted and cautious, as if she wasn't sure how to treat her or what to say to her.

Lisa couldn't complain that Alex neglected her. He was as attentive as any new bridegroom might be expected to be. He saw to it that she had everything she could wish for to ensure her enjoyment of the delicious meal, but, for some reason, Lisa's nerves grew tight again and she found it difficult to swallow. Madeline's voice became an incomprehensible drone, Alex's insistence that she ate more an intolerable pressure, while the soft-footed servants transformed into so many jailers she had a hysterical desire to escape from.

She could have wept with relief when the meal was over and a sudden commotion outside heralded the well-wishers Alex had mentioned earlier. Having to face a crowd of strangers didn't somehow seem as daunting as having to endure perhaps another few hours of Madame Demetris's stringent company.

'That will be half the island, many of your own tenants, Alex, coming to wish you good luck,' she heard Madame saying, her voice cool. 'They always believed you would be married here so I hope you aren't going to disappoint them further by refusing to see them.'

'No, why should I?' Alex said blandly. 'It's really up to Lisa.'

Though Lisa couldn't be sure what lay behind his apparent consideration for her, she said quickly, 'I'd love to meet them.' But as they went outside she sensed, as the geniality faded from his face, that he wasn't really relishing having to present her to his people as his dearly loved bride when he secretly considered his marriage a mockery.

It was dark, with the moon just rising, but many of those who had come carried flares and lanterns. To Lisa the courtyard seemed full of people and, as she and Alex appeared, the low murmur of voices rose to a positive crescendo. There was something primitive about the scene, the lights, the laughter, the flickering gleam of reckless eyes and white teeth through the darkness, the high, excited exuberance of warm congratulations.

She clung a little closer to Alex's arm as he murmured something to his aunt who nodded and went back into the house and almost immediately, to Lisa's astonishment and the delight of the crowd, tables were set up on the stone flags and laden with food and drink.

They were feted from all sides and, as Alex introduced her, as he had done earlier to his house servants, Lisa was the focus of all eyes and couldn't help feeling surprised and touched by the consensus of general approval. Alex's countrymen, she soon discovered, were very kind and friendly and she was warmed by their whole-hearted acceptance of her. There was none of the sly whispering which had transpired when she had married Philip and, though the circumstances of her second marriage might be far from ideal, she couldn't help contrasting it with that other one and feeling grateful for the difference.

Alex played the part of a happy bridegroom well. He replied to the numerous toasts and drank his share of wine. Food and drink disappeared in great quantities and there was dancing, too, the music being supplied by local musicians. Lisa danced with Alex but she wasn't familiar with Greek folk dancing and while these were being performed she was content to sit and watch.

The hours passed and the night grew wilder. Lisa was beginning to feel rather dazed by it all when Alex took her arm in unspoken command and she slipped away with him. No one seemed to notice their going and, once inside the house, they might have been in another world, it was so quiet.

'It's the way the house is built,' Alex explained, as she commented on this.

'Did your father build it?' she asked as he drew her swiftly into their bedroom and closed the door.

'No.' His voice sounded thick, as if he wasn't concentrating on what he was saying. 'My mother lived here a few years before she died but my father never did.'

It seemed to Lisa strangely disconcerting that they had never discussed their respective parents, other than by casual reference, until now. And now wasn't time, as she could see from the smouldering expression in Alex's eyes.

Feeling scorched by it, she began taking off her watch with unsteady fingers. It wasn't easy to reconcile the love she had for him, the overwhelming need to give herself to him, with the kind of feelings she knew he had for her. There was desire in his eyes but nothing else, only the ravaging impatience of a man consumed by a passion he has waited too long to appease. This, and the amount of wine he had drunk would, she feared, cancel out any of the tender consideration he might normally have shown his bride. And, believing she was experienced, he wouldn't think it necessary to be gentle with her.

When he flung off his jacket and swiftly closed the distance she had put between them, she turned to him, once more attempting to explain her innocence, but even as she opened her mouth to begin, his own swooped on to it, taking it in a kiss which demolished every other thought in her mind, other than how much she wanted him. And, if his mouth was ravaging in its demands, so were his hands. She had thought, this evening, in the few times she had allowed herself to think of it, that he would undress her slowly, between kisses which might be indulgent. On several occasions she had noticed his compassion for the old and infirm and small children. She had suspected that under Alex's arrogance and pride might lie a heart much softer than people generally supposed, but she was soon to find she was mistaken. Without mercy he plundered her lips while his hands, having fondled all the bare flesh he could find, tore off her dress. He was oblivious to her sharp gasp as the zip caught on her skin, and his black eyes were filled with a volume of desire she couldn't even meet, let alone protest to.

'You can't deny me now,' he rasped, his burning glance leaving her trembling.

She had no intention of denying him. Despite the misgivings which were always with her, she was too aware of her own cravings to reject him, now they were married.

'No,' she breathed, and he gave her no more time to even try and tell him what she had been doing her best to tell him for weeks, and, as his mouth triumphantly found the throbbing pulse at the base of her throat, she couldn't even remember what it was.

He seemed intent on devouring her, as he flung her on the bed and came down beside her. She heard words which were slurred as his eyes ravished the rich curves of her body. He had seen her like this before but had never looked at her with such complete satisfaction. When she made a soft, responsive sound, the mouth he lowered to hers hardened with sudden violence. Lisa shivered with a delight that was both innocent and knowledgeable, and, as her tumultuous longing broke through her virginal reticence, her fears died, along with her puny resistance.

She clung to him, her arms sliding around his neck, her fingers pushing through his hair as his kisses grew more insistent. She wanted to explore his body, as he was exploring hers, but the relentless haste he was in didn't allow it. Keeping an arm clasped over her, as if afraid she might escape, he pulled off his own clothing, swiftly revealing the desire he felt for her. He lay against her, hard and erect, savouring her hungrily, letting his hand run over slender thighs while his mouth began teasing taut nipples.

Lisa's breath caught as a searing heat flashed through her stomach and her instant response destroyed the last of his restraint. Small moans escaped her as his mouth opened and his teeth bit, as he aroused her with a sensual expertise which soon had her twisting convulsively against him.

She felt completely disorientated, never having made love with anyone before. Her body arched and leapt under his, her heart raced, her breasts swelled against the roughness of his chest as she abandoned herself to the unspoken commands of his mouth and hands. When his voice came, her senses were so inflamed she could scarcely hear what he was saying.

'Lisa, I want you now.'

Her eyelids were so heavy she found it difficult to raise them to tell him she wanted him too. But she was going to tell him until she saw the savage desire in his face and nothing else. At once she went rigid with panic. She wanted him, God knew how much, but not like this!

Fiercely she began pushing against him without

stopping to think, desperate to try and explain while not realising he was bound to misunderstand. His eyes lit with a ruthless rage as he thought she was trying to evade him again. With a low cry, he forced himself on her, rendering her helpless against the heavy thrust of his thighs.

She felt him flinch, even before she screamed in anguish, while instinct told her it was too late. In an instant it was over, he wasn't hurting any more, but she was too stunned to feel anything but his mounting passion culminating and washing over her, leaving her strangely unsatisfied. She lay panting, half sobbing, hating him for hurting her, while feeling cheated that he hadn't apologised and had patience with her, for she had caught a brief glimpse of something wonderful that might have been hers if he had.

She was still burning with unsatisfed yearning when he put a little distance between them. If he had been slightly drunk before, he certainly wasn't now, as his glacial expression clearly indicated.

Harshly he snapped, 'I wouldn't have hurt you if I'd known you were a virgin and you hadn't struggled. I want an explanation, Lisa!'

'I tried to tell you,' she retorted wildly, swallowing tears, 'but you wouldn't listen. You were so convinced that all you'd heard about me was true.'

'How could I believe otherwise?' He glared. 'I couldn't discount all the stories and I knew what Philip Fielding was like.'

'I could understand your feelings to begin with,' she choked, 'but surely after getting to know me, you must have had your doubts?'

He wounded her even more by asking curtly, 'Did you lead all your other men on, as you did me, always promising what I had to force you into giving? Which doesn't explain Philip, of course, why your marriage to him was never consummated. From what I recall of him, he'd be a man with all the usual urges.'

'Philip married me for convenience,' she whispered tautly, her face bleak as she remembered. 'He wanted a wife to camouflage his affair with a married woman, Gilda Grant.'

'So that's why she hates you?' Rage rekindled in his eyes. 'And you were willing to go along with it, to sell your soul, if not your body, for money.'

'No!'

'Now I can understand why Fielding didn't leave you anything. It was a business arrangement—he considered you'd been well enough paid.'

'Alex . . .!'

'Be quiet!' he snarled. 'You were prepared to risk having an old man forcing his attentions on you.'

'He didn't . . .'

'As has just been proved,' he conceded harshly. 'It's ironical, is it not, that I got a virgin, after all, but even more of an adventuress than I had thought.'

Lisa bowed her head, feeling his words like physical blows. What was the use of trying to tell him about her parents when, as before, he refused to listen? And if he didn't feel any trust for her, if it never occurred to him to pause and wonder if there couldn't have been extenuating circumstances regarding her marriage to Philip, what use to her was a faith that demanded absolute proof of everything? Besides, if it came to that, she couldn't really give him any. Only Edward might still have a copy of the agreement which Philip had arranged to have drawn up for her parents, but she certainly wasn't going to ask him for it.

'I suppose,' she choked, 'you don't want anything more to do with me?'

His mouth twisted humourlessly as he stared at her with burning eyes. 'I've learned little I didn't already know, or which makes me want you less. That you came to me untouched is a bonus I didn't look for but I will still get rid of you when I tire of you . . . However, that won't be for some time.'

Lisa's eyes filled with helpless tears as she whispered, 'You must be insane.'

'Possibly,' he agreed indifferently, his arms going around her again. 'One day I'll come to my senses again but, meanwhile, you're in my blood and I have no intention of worrying about it or denying myself. I want you, my darling.' Both his eyes and voice softened incredibly. 'You delight me and I want you to share that delight.'

Her face whitened as she tried to twist away from him, accusing wildly, 'There was nothing delightful in what we shared.'

'That was because, for you, it was the first time.'

'No!' she insisted, still struggling as he would have pulled her closer. 'I don't believe it.'

He paused, noting the tear-stained cheeks, apprehensive eyes and trembling mouth, then, with a rough exclamation, he scooped her up and carried her to the bathroom.

'Let's have a shower,' he said, stepping with her under it and turning on the jets.

Letting her slide to her feet, he still held her but Lisa lost her desire to fight him. As the warm water poured over them, she was soothed by it yet aware of other, more disturbing feelings intruding. Her senses traitorously began concentrating on the hardness of the male body beside her, the sharp heat of Alex's mouth against her neck, the dampness of his flesh against hers. It became an intolerable pleasure against which she lost the ability to fight.

After a while, during which he never stopped kissing her, he lifted her out and began drying her with a warm towel. A few moments later he threw it aside and carried her back to bed. He didn't seem in the least concerned that they were both naked and by this time Lisa was feeling too relaxed to be concerned either. All she wished to do, when he lay down beside her, was to curl up against him and go to sleep.

Smothering a tiny yawn, she tried to creep under the sheet and close her eyes, but he wouldn't allow it.

'Later,' he smiled, his arms tightening as he began kissing her again. 'The more I get of you, the more I want,' he said thickly, 'and you're going to feel the same way about me. I hurt you before but it won't be like that this time. Let me show you.'

With tender slowness he turned her on her back and, unable to prevent herself, Lisa forgot how she had suffered and threw her arms around his neck. She could feel herself responding wherever he touched her as he continued to caress her with his hands and mouth. The blood began pounding through her veins, generating a heat which became so intolerable that she felt she was on fire. As the flames from it consumed her, her heart leapt in panic then surrendered without further struggle. Her eyes closed, her breathing was shallow and rapid as she became lost to everything but her own rising passion.

He was setting the pace, going carefully this time, his own passion tightly controlled until he could be sure of her absolute co-operation. Sensing when she was helpless against the surge of desire that scorched through her and that her need was as great as his, with infinite patience he pushed between her knees and possessed her.

Lisa's breath caught wildly as he took her gently but forcefully. Through a haze she heard him groan her name before all her senses became concentrated on one goal. This time, unlike the last time, when he had satisfied his own needs, regardless, now he took her with him all the way. There was a blaze of almost intolerable pleasure as she reached heights and experienced feelings more rapturous than anything she could ever have imagined. She felt Alex, shuddering and empty, still resting his full weight on her, but she only wrapped him tighter, welcoming his continuing closeness.

She woke to a sun high in the sky, after a night spent in her husband's arms. She couldn't remember the half of it—when had she fallen asleep? She only remembered the incredible delight.

Throwing out a bemused hand to touch him, she suddenly realised he wasn't there. Thinking he must have been up for hours, she was startled to see him emerging from his dressing-room, wearing only a short robe. Just then a maid knocked and entered with a breakfast tray.

Wishing Alex had warned her, Lisa managed to hide herself, if not her blushes, under a sheet until the girl had gone. She tried not to glare at him as she realised he was laughing at her discomposure.

'You don't have to be embarrassed,' he growled, when they were alone again. 'On our islands, getting married, making love, making babies is considered as natural as the wind that blows. No one tries to control the meltemi—or love.'

Lisa felt herself stiffen and the colour faded from her face. Before she could stop herself, she found herself responding bitterly. 'Love has nothing to do with our union though, has it, Alex! You married me in order to save your face after making a mistake at Athens airport. That, and probably an irrational desire to possess me.'

CHAPTER NINE

FOR a moment, believing Alex was going to hit her, Lisa thought she had gone too far, but whatever rage he felt was swiftly controlled and he merely shrugged as he picked up the tray the maid had left.

'What's the matter, Lisa?' he mocked, sitting down beside her and pouring her some coffee. 'Don't tell me that making love doesn't agree with you. Last night, once you got over your little inhibitions, I got the distinct impression that it did.'

'You could be mistaken,' she retorted tersely, feeling bitterly hurt that he enjoyed pouring scorn on something that, to her, had seemed incredibly beautiful. 'You made me respond but that doesn't alter the fact that I still hate you for what you've done to me.'

His face darkened forbiddingly as he stared at her. 'Only a few weeks ago you told me you loved me.'

'So you keep reminding me.'

'Your feelings can't have changed that much?'

Lisa stared back at him angrily. She was also angry that she couldn't deny it while knowing, somehow, she had to convince him it wasn't true. Once he thought he had any kind of power over her, her life might be even more intolerable than it was now. 'You surely didn't expect me to go on loving you after the way you treated me?' she cried.

'Methinks the lady doth protest too much,' he gibed, not appearing to notice the devious way she had countered his question. 'You certainly seemed fond enough of me last night.'

He cheeks flamed, even more than they had done when the maid came in. 'I don't want to talk about it.'

His eyes narrowed threateningly. 'If I had time, I'd

make you talk about it but, already, I've missed an important call and Paul will be ringing any minute.'

'I thought you had cleared up all your affairs.' She frowned, as he got off the bed.

'There's always something,' he shrugged, 'I can seldom escape altogether.

She wasn't sure what made her call after him, when she had implied that, as far as she was concerned, the subject was closed. 'What can it matter whether I care for you or not when you intend getting rid of me?'

'I didn't say it mattered,' he drawled over his shoulder. 'I'm quite convinced you married me for what you could get out of me, the same as you did Fielding.'

'You can't believe that . . .!' she said despairingly.

'Lisa!' In two strides he was beside her again, grasping her slumped shoulders with hands that hurt and eyes that burned. 'I want you, I've told you I don't know why, but not permanently, so whatever I believe about your former marriage is scarcely relevant. I suggest that, like me, you enjoy what we have while it lasts.'

'I don't want your money, anyway,' she muttered aggressively to hide her pain.

'Good.' His eyes flashed derisively. 'Now that we understand each other, my darling, we should get on famously.' His hands tightened as he stared at her tumbled hair and quivering mouth and he had visibly to wrench himself away. 'I'll see you later,' he said thickly.

After he had gone, Lisa rose and dressed, dismayed to find it almost lunch time. Hastily she made the bed, thinking, that as it was so late, the maids might forget about it. Alex's dressing-room, when she peered in, was a mess, his clothes scattered all over the place. She sighed and resolved to tidy up for him later, if no one else did.

After lunch, during which Madame Demetris chattered incessantly about the previous evening's celebrations, Alex returned to his study and his aunt, after talking to Lisa a few more minutes, went to her room to rest.

Lisa wandered aimlessly into the hall then decided she needed some fresh air. The sun was high overhead and it was hot but suddenly she couldn't bear to stay indoors. Without bothering to do more than find her hat and sunglasses, she left the house.

For a while she explored the gardens, amazed by their extent and the size of the swimming pool she found there. The cool depth of it was inviting but she abandoned it in favour of the sea. Tomorrow she would get up early and have a swim but, this afternoon, she was keener to explore.

The blue Aegean beckoned, and as she stood on the cliffs leading down to the shore, she wondered exactly where Sanara lay. The Greek islands were very well known and popular but she felt hopelessly ignorant about them, a state of affairs she hoped to correct. She was rapidly learning how beautiful they were, but was determined to learn more. Before she left.

As this thought brought back Alex's cruel words, tears sprang to her eyes and, having tried to forget what he had said, she was impatient of her wet cheeks. Stoically, until now, she had managed to keep at bay everything that had happened between them during the night but her tears mocked her with proof that she hadn't succeeded. What was the use of trying to follow Alex's advice—to enjoy her new life while it lasted, if her aching heart wouldn't let her?

Thrusting her hands deep in the pockets of the yellow sundress she wore, she set her chin at a more determined angle and ran down to the beach. She didn't know if the beach was private but there was no one else about and the white sands were so tempting that she found a shady spot beside some rocks and stretched out, hoping the warmth of the sand combined with the soothing sound of the sea would soon help her to feel better.

It was here that Alex found her. He must have moved softly for she didn't hear him approaching and was startled, on opening her eyes, to find him leaning against the rocks watching her. 'Oh! I didn't hear you,' she cried.

'I think you were asleep,' he teased.

Dazed, she blinked at him, realising she was in no position to deny it. To her surprise, for she had only seen him impeccably dressed, his only garment was a pair of cut off blue jeans. Her breath caught at the tall, bare strength of his body, the breadth of his chest under the shadowing of dark hair that covered it.

'Where are you off to?' she gulped.

He smiled lazily, holding out a hand. 'To look over my boat, actually. Before I got diverted by a pair of beautiful legs. Want to come?'

'I'd love to!' Immediately she forgot his harshness of the morning, his brooding silence over lunch, and didn't think to hide her delight as she took his proferred hand and walked beside him, down to the sea.

The boat, a sizeable cabin cruiser, was anchored by a small jetty. Lisa fell in love with it at first sight.

'Like it?' he asked.

'It's beautiful!' she breathed.

'Not as beautiful as you,' he said thickly, turning her into his arms and kissing her. A few minutes later he reluctantly released her. 'I must get something done before I take you below. That may really test my forbearance.'

'You don't have to show me around.' She flushed. 'I can manage myself.' But when he commanded her to wait, he was in such a good mood that she obeyed. She was in no hurry and she suspected he was only teasing her. For a while she pottered about the deck then merely sat and watched him checking things.

When he eventually finished and said he was ready for the conducted tour, she went with him eagerly. The cabins were so comfortable and spacious that she couldn't help commenting how lovely it must be to go for a sailing holiday.

'We'll see.' Alex shrugged, picking up a bag he had carried to the beach and tossing it to her. As she caught it then glanced at him enquiringly, he explained, 'It's your swimsuit, one of them, anyway. Put it on and we'll have a swim.'

He seemed to take it for granted that she would want to for he didn't wait for a reply. Thinking with delight of the warm, buoyant waters of the bay, Lisa hurried to do as she was bid, but when she joined him again, on deck, she found him still in his jeans.

'Why haven't you changed?' She frowned. 'Aren't you going in?'

'Of course,' he said, 'but I don't usually wear anything, unless I have guests.'

'D—don't I warrant the same consideration?' she stammered, cheeks pink.

'You have to earn it,' he retorted more sharply, and the day was suddenly colder as she realised all the things he thought her guilty of were never far from his mind.

Having, she thought, deliberately embarrassed her by letting her believe he intended bathing in the nude, she could have hit him when he dived in beside her without removing his jeans. She refused to be amused when he laughed and asked, 'Aren't you disappointed?'

It was impossible to be cross for long, though, in such ideal conditions. Soon she was laughing with him, as they swam and dived and played. An hour passed in a flash, with Lisa enjoying herself so much that she immediately protested when Alex declared she had been in long enough.

'I don't want to tire you,' he said, as they climbed back on board.

'I don't feel the least bit tired,' she assured him, brushing the long, wet hair from her face and thinking how much she loved him. She couldn't complain that he hadn't been nice to her, this afternoon. Apart from one or two gibes, he had been very pleasant. She concentrated on this and tried not to remember he had no real feelings for her and meant to eventually get rid of her.

As she went back to the cabin to get dressed again, her heart jerked as he followed and began peeling off his wet jeans.

'What are you doing?' she choked.

'What does it look like?' he mocked, stepping out of them as if he wasn't aware how all her pulses were stampeding. 'You can always look the other way, but we do happen to be married.'

If only she could look the other way. If only her eyes didn't seem glued to him and she wasn't being rendered slowly helpless by the gathering heat in her limbs. Then suddenly, as he turned, she was in his arms, without being conscious of who had taken the first step, and his lips were plundering hers while his hands went straight to her breasts.

'You want me,' he muttered, more of a statement than a question as he felt her instant response.

How could she hide her overwhelming desire for him when it rose in her so fast she hadn't a chance of concealing it. She could feel the same desire consuming Alex as well, as he picked her up and carried her to one of the bunks, but she sensed a trace of resentment behind his ardour. He wanted to distance himself from either her or his own emotions, she wasn't sure which. He didn't have to express in words that he considered his passion for her unreasonable and was fighting it. The simple act of possessing her should, in his opinion, have lessened his need of her and she could read the harsh impatience in his face that this hadn't proved enough.

There was little gentleness in him as he practically threw her on to the bunk and came down on top of her. Ruthlessly he crushed her mouth open under his, as if tasting her thoroughly might cure him of his addiction. When it didn't, he took her swiftly and fiercely and didn't stop until she was shuddering and moaning mindlessly as the clamour in her own body grew too overpowering to control.

The climax came quickly, a deluge of sensation which left Lisa clinging to him tighter and gasping for air. She could feel his heart thudding against hers, his breath warm on her throat, his hard body still pressing hers into the mattress.

Her mouth felt soft and swollen, her skin as hot and damp as his. She felt the blood begin to throb through her veins again as he shifted off her and cupped her breast in his hand. Bending, he caught her nipple between his teeth and her fingers tangled helplessly in his hair as a searing heat flashed through her stomach and she felt the need in him rapidly rebuilding again. Soon she was lost to everything but the insistence of rising pleasure and sensuous demand and she wrapped her arms around him tightly as, once more, he fitted her trembling body into his own.

It was after six when they walked back to the house. Lisa was reluctant to leave the boat, wanting to cling to the idyllic hours they had spent there. They had made love, slept, and made love again when they woke then discovered it was growing late and remembered Madeline would be expecting them to join her for dinner.

The helicopter came as a surprise. As they walked up the steep incline to the gardens, they saw it coming in from the sea. Alex frowned as he watched it landing on the helipad but his expression changed to one of pleasure as he apparently recognised who it was.

'Is it Paul?' Lisa asked uncertainly.

'No,' Alex replied briefly. 'It's Stefan Palides, a neighbour of mine, and his daughter, Letha, unless I'm mistaken.'

As they drew nearer, the two people who got out of

the aircraft noticed them and hurried towards them, the man holding out his hand.

'Alex!' he beamed. 'This is a surprise. Letha and I thought we'd drop in and see your aunt but we believed you'd be elsewhere, on your honeymoon.' He glanced at Lisa. 'Is this your wife?'

'Yes.' Alex introduced her then invited Stefan and his daughter, whose name Lisa was certain she had heard before but couldn't place, to join them for dinner.

Both the Palideses accepted and, as they reached the house, Madame Demetris made no attempt to conceal her delight when she saw who Alex and Lisa had with them.

'Go and get dressed,' Alex murmured to Lisa, 'I'll join you shortly.'

Lisa took this to mean he would be following almost immediately, but though she didn't hurry she had completed her toilet and was waiting, long before he did. She was beginning to wonder what was keeping him when he appeared.

His eyes smouldered as they wandered over her slender figure but he sounded impatient, rather than amorous as he asked, 'Why didn't you come back to the lounge? Letha would like to talk to you.'

'You said you would join me,' she reminded him. 'I wasn't sure what to do.'

'Next time use a bit more initiative,' he retorted, going into his dressing-room and closing the door.

Bewildered by his coolness and odd behaviour, Lisa banged the suite door, in what she supposed was childish retaliation on her way out. She couldn't imagine what she and Letha would have in common. Letha was beautiful and obviously spoiled, and would be much more interested, Lisa suspected, in talking to Alex.

Alex wasn't uninterested either. The thought came to Lisa like a douche of cold water, as she recalled the gleam in his black eyes as they had rested on Stefan's daughter. It had been distinctly proprietorial, a look which, until now, she had thought reserved for herself.

It wasn't until halfway through dinner that she suddenly remembered that Letha was the name of the girl he had talked of marrying. Shock rushed through her and she wondered how she could have forgotten. It couldn't be coincidence. And if she had doubted her intuition, wasn't there enough evidence to be found in Letha's pouting glances, her father's reproachful looks and Madeline's distinctly apologetic demeanour?

Bleakly she noted the attention Alex was showering on the girl. He had her sitting beside him where his wife should have been. Lisa, sitting at the opposite end of the long table, reached blindly for her glass, and meeting his hard eyes as she raised it to her lips, knew that her optimism of the afternoon had been too presumptuous. Alex obviously had no intention of letting her remain in his life any longer than was strictly necessary.

When the visitors had left and Alex retired to his study, Lisa decided to go to bed and asked Madame to excuse her. Her head had begun to throb and she rubbed her temples wearily as she started getting undressed. There was so much to think about yet she didn't know where to begin. Last night, and this afternoon, with the heady sensation of Alex's hard body beside her and the magic of his lovemaking swamping her mind, she had forgotten about everything else. She certainly shouldn't have forgotten that nothing had really changed.

The minutes ticked laboriously by as she searched unsuccessfully for a solution to the predicament she was in. A shower relaxed her physically but she still felt too tense to sleep. Then she remembered the state of Alex's dressing-room and decided to see what she could do about it, in the hope that the effort involved might tire her.

The maids hadn't been in, his clothes were still lying

all over the place. This surprised her for she had noticed he was usually meticulous when it came to putting things away. The suit he had worn for their wedding looked absolutely abandoned where it was flung over a chair. Swallowing an irrational tear, she was lifting it up to hang it away when a long envelope fell from one of the pockets.

'Damn!' she muttered under her breath, making a dive for it and, because she had her arms full, picking it up the wrong way so that the contents fell out of it. With another impatient mutter, she flung the suit back down and grabbed the piece of legal looking paper and was just about to thrust it back into its envelope when something made her pause and stare at it.

She didn't know what made her feel suddenly convinced that the document had to do with her, but not being in the habit of reading other people's letters, she looked at it for quite a time before she found the courage to open it. Then she immediately wished she hadn't.

It was all there, everything Alex had threatened her with but which she had foolishly thought had gone no further than that. The printed words danced before her anguished eyes but were still inescapable. Yet they wounded her so much that after the first few lines she had to force herself to go on.

The first clause stated that she, Lisa Andreas, voluntarily renounced any claims she felt she might have on the estate of her husband, and was willing to accept only what he was prepared to give her when they were divorced. The second clause stipulated that she should be willing to grant Alex a divorce whenever he wished. The third condition was that any children from their union should live with Alex, with access granted to Lisa only when he saw fit.

It contained a lot of legal jargon which Lisa barely understood, but she knew she had got the gist of it. At the bottom of the sheet was a blank dotted line where

the person concerned was requested to sign. Lisa was
still staring at it in a kind of paralysed horror when she
heard Alex calling her name.

'Lisa . . .!' He walked in on her then halted abruptly.
'What on earth are you doing?'

Lisa felt so sick that her stomach began protesting
and she had to press a hand to it before she could
speak. 'R-reading this,' she whispered, her face ashen.

A vein throbbed dangerously at his temple. 'You've
been going through my pockets.'

'No.' Briefly she closed her eyes until the room
stopped swimming. 'Everything was such a mess. I was
tidying up your suits when this fell out of your pocket.'

The paper was ripped from her hands. 'Well I hope
you feel better for not minding your own business.'

'But it is my business—how can you say that?'
Helpless tears in her eyes, she glared at him. 'I know
you said you would have an agreement drawn up but I
didn't really believe that even you could be so cold-
blooded.'

He frowned as he met her accusing eyes. 'I'm not
cold-blooded, Lisa,' he murmured, as though trying to
reason with her. 'Any man in my position has to
safeguard his interests. A marriage contract is nothing
to get in a state about. There would have been one,
whoever I married.'

'Would Letha have agreed to such terms?'

Twin spots of colour spread over his cheekbones.
'What do you know about her?'

'Just what I guessed. You mentioned her name, in
London, though you may not remember.'

'She need not concern you,' he muttered in a low
voice. 'Lisa, for God's sake, listen to me.'

'She's not my concern, I agree.' Ignoring his plea,
Lisa went on wildly. 'I realise marriage contracts are
no new thing but I don't believe, if you'd married her,
you would have stipulated the same terms.'

'Because you aren't the same people.'

'Thank you!' she choked.

He glared at her and while she could see that, like herself, he was under a great deal of strain, she couldn't feel sorry for him.

'Lisa!' He held out a hand. 'Come here.'

Angrily she thrust his hand from her. 'I don't think I could bear to touch you. Just how long were you going to keep that horrible agreement before you showed it to me?'

'I hadn't decided.' Anger darkened his face at her tone. 'But for one or two things, I might have torn the whole thing up.'

Her voice trembled with sudden fury. 'It's not just one or two things though, is it, Alex? You have a whole range of things lined up against me. I don't know how you could make love to me, having so little respect for me. It makes me feel sick even to think about it.'

'You knew all along what I wanted, Lisa,' he said tightly. 'Respect has nothing to do with what I feel for you. I don't know how long it will take me to tire myself of you but, until I do, you will be well enough looked after. I don't see that you have anything to complain of.'

For a moment she stared at him, stunned by such unbelievable arrogance. 'What I have to complain of!' she reiterated, incensed. 'You must think me completely insensitive. The first clause in that contract, I mightn't have objected to, though I was hurt that you felt you had to put it in writing. The second seems irrelevant, but the third, about any children we may have, I'd never agree to, not even if you tried to beat me into submission.'

'You don't think I'd let my sons be brought up in the back streets of London, do you?'

'Wherever our sons lived,' she amended bitterly, 'they would be brought up properly, but I would never leave them.'

'You could be pregnant now,' he said harshly.

'It's possible.' A painful flush stained the paleness of her cheeks. 'We've been careless, but I'll take no more risks from now on. I won't sleep with you again, Alex.'

'You're being unreasonable,' he retorted, between his teeth.

'I won't deliberately have children you would force me to leave,' she said bravely.

His brows lowered ominously while a muscle jerked in his jaw. 'You won't get rid of me that easily,' he said angrily. 'While you are my wife, you will sleep with me, nowhere else. After all, apart from a foolish fiasco over a piece of paper, nothing has changed.'

Something blocked Lisa's throat as she stared at him, the slight hope that he would take her in his arms and tell her he had made a ghastly mistake, dying in her heart. He couldn't talk to her like this if he cared anything for her. Unless, her hopes revived a little, unless he secretly regretted the contract but was too proud to tell her?

'Alex,' she murmured hesitantly, 'there was a lot of controversy between us before we were married, and I realise how easy it is to let bitterness lead one to make mistakes. You didn't show me the contract straight away. Was it because, despite what you said, you really intended tearing it up?'

He stood taut, arms by his sides, his body entirely still. For a moment he looked strangely vulnerable, like a man being attacked yet unable to see the enemy. Then his face hardened. 'And put myself in your late husband's position? My mother . . .' He broke off, his scowl deepening.

Lisa's blue eyes darkened with misery as he seemed to stamp on her olive branch. 'You were saying something about your mother?' she prompted hollowly.

'Forget it,' he retorted brusquely.

'That's all I can do, I suppose,' she said tautly. 'You're so determined to shut me out.'

Running an impatient hand through his dark hair, he

snapped, 'I still don't see what you have to complain about. While you're married to me you have my name and protection and I don't think you could even convince yourself that you find me abhorrent.'

Looking into his saturnine, mocking face, she visibly recoiled. 'I may not have done,' she acknowledged, 'but I'm not sure how I feel now.'

They surveyed each other warily. She took in the deepening lines around his mouth, his shuttered expression, and saw he was fighting to control his temper. He seemed less than impressed by her ambivalent response.

Gentle hands, which she failed to avoid, clamped on her slender shoulders. 'You've had a shock,' he soothed. 'You found that damned paper and you're letting it worry you unnecessarily. Why don't you just forget about it and come to bed?'

Their eyes clashed head on again and she felt dizzy from the impact of his powerful personality, but she wouldn't back down. Her pride had taken all the beating it was going to. Disregarding the turbulent emotions churning inside her, she retorted through dry lips, 'I don't want anything more to do with you.'

'You might have changed your mind about loving me,' he rasped, black eyes leaping, 'but you can't so easily ignore what there is between us. We ignite immediately, you light fires inside me I can't put out, so don't imagine for a moment that I'll allow you to abandon me.' The coaxing tone returned. 'You were inexperienced when you came to me, but you must have realised that what we have is very rare. You'd be cheating yourself as much as me by turning your back on it.'

'You intend to!' she cried angrily.

'Not for some time,' he said thickly.

She sighed as he went on holding her, staring at her with burning eyes. He wanted her and knew she wanted him but she felt suddenly cold that he should consider this enough. That it wasn't for her, she was finding out the hard way. She had been very foolish even to hope that it would be.

Trying to put all the resolve she felt into her voice, she said, 'I'll stay with you but I won't sleep with you. I haven't changed my mind.'

His molten glance sliced through her. 'It's no use taking that attitude. Dammit, Lisa,' he swore softly, 'I didn't want to insist on my rights but I won't be made a fool of. You knew what you were doing when you married me. It's too late now to change your mind. About anything.'

He was a devil, she thought agonisingly, as with a strangled cry of protest, she tried to push him away. Her struggles merely aroused his temper further and his tightening grip hurt as he picked her up and carried her through to the bedroom and deposited her on the bed.

'Let me go!' she gasped, her arms flaying as she fought to free herself. She stared up into that handsome face above her, terrified by the smouldering light in his eyes which had darkened to the colour of a stormy sea, his sensual mouth hard with passion. He was so powerful he frightened her and she recognised the futility of fighting him.

Ignoring her pleas, he began kissing her, at first savagely, then more gently as she began slowly responding. Then, as though sensing victory was within his grasp, he went on kissing her until her control broke completely and with a helpless moan she wound her arms around his neck. Vaguely she realised what she was inviting but was unable to stop herself, knowing that only total surrender would give her some relief from the burning torment inside her. Yet when it came, with his urgent and passionate possession of her, she realised hollowly that he didn't love her and was only interested in imposing his will on her.

In the first light of dawn, she awoke and lay gazing at him as he slept quietly beside her. Even in sleep he was able to alter her breathing and she felt a welling tide of pain and frustration that this should be so. He had married her, it seemed, without any other purpose than to eventually get rid of her. Last night she had fought him but he had destroyed even her passive resistance, making her yield to him as wildly as she had done on the boat. Now she felt bitterly ashamed of herself and knew she must get away from him before it was too late. Partly she blamed herself for having married him but she had learned long ago that a solution to a problem was rarely found by mulling over past mistakes.

Leaving Alex still sleeping, she slipped out of bed and found a bikini, hoping that a swim might clear her head. The house was quiet and, outside, it was too early for even the gardeners to be about. Lisa had the place to herself until Alex joined her.

She didn't welcome his presence but there was nothing she could do about it. His splendid physique, as usual, made her heart race but she hoped, if he noticed, he put it down to her exertions in the pool.

'Wake me another morning, before you go out,' he growled, diving expertly into the water.

'You were sleeping,' she replied as he came up. 'I didn't want to disturb you.'

He glanced at her closed face sideways. 'That's no excuse. I'd rather be disturbed that way than wake up myself and discover you had gone.'

'Were you worried?'

'Until I discovered where you were.'

'Poor Alex,' she taunted bitterly, 'are you always so anxious over your—possessions?'

His eyes glinted warningly but he merely retorted, 'Some of them.'

As if to punish her, his glance lingered on the swell of her breasts, and heat immediately began surging through her veins. Drawing a quick breath, she dived past him, where he was treading water, into the pool again. He was going to pretend nothing had happened. She kept a firm grip on her anger while trying to control the silly trembling feeling which the sight of him always evoked. She felt she was on an emotional seesaw and the strain was proving too much. Unhappily, she turned her head to look back at him, her expression so desolate that she saw him frown, but his eyes were so completely unrevealing that she thought a shutter had come down.

A few minutes later when a servant came to inform him there was a call for him in the study, he left her without another glance, but he did join her afterwards for breakfast.

'Was your call about business?' she asked, risking sounding curious in order to break the uncomfortable silence between them. It seemed he had only joined her for the sake of appearances and she wished he had stayed in his study.

'Yes,' he replied absently, buttering one of Filana's newly baked croissants which Lisa found so delicious and spreading it liberally with cherry jam. 'I'm afraid I'm going to be busy all morning. Will you be able to amuse yourself?'

'I think so,' she said coolly, wanting some time to think and refusing to wonder what the household thought about a bride being left so much alone on her honeymoon. 'I'll probably talk to your aunt. Somehow I don't seem to have exchanged more than two words with her since we came.'

For a long moment he stared at her, frowning, then he merely nodded and said, 'I'll see you at lunch then,' as he rose and left her.

When Lisa finished her own breakfast—which consisted of much less than Alex had eaten, she chatted for a few minutes with Filana, who seemed eager to please her, then went out into the grounds. She had been quite sincere when she had told Alex she would like to talk to his aunt but as the housekeeper had assured her that Madame wouldn't be up for at least another hour, there didn't seem much point in just hanging about.

Having heard Alex on the telephone as she passed the study door, she didn't believe he would attempt to follow her and decided to explore a little further than she had done the day before. At the back of her mind was the hazy notion that somewhere there might be someone willing to help her to get off the island and back to Athens. Wasn't there always someone willing to do almost anything for money?

Any hopes she was entertaining in this direction were, however, swiftly destroyed when, on her way to the nearest village, to which Filana had unwittingly directed her, she sensed instinctively that she was being followed. Sure enough, on glancing quickly over her shoulder, she saw a man whom she had taken to be one of Alex's gardeners, a few yards behind her. She had noticed him particularly for he had been tidying the grounds near the edge of the cliff while she had been on the beach, yesterday.

Biting her lip in bitter frustration, she pretended to wander around a little then returned to the villa. The village would probably be full of Alex's paid spies as well, or at least full of people only too willing to inform on her. It would be a sheer waste of time going anywhere near it! It might be more rewarding and less humiliating to settle for a quiet morning with Madame Demetris.

CHAPTER TEN

SHE found Madame on the terrace and sank down beside her on one of the luxurious canopied chairs. A maid was serving coffee and Lisa accepted a cup gratefully. Frustration and unhappiness mustn't agree with her for she felt tense and exhausted close to tears. The coffee scalded her throat as she drank it too hot but she welcomed the physical pain which diverted her attention from the way her heart was aching. The morning appeared to have defeated her although she wasn't sure, if she had reached the village, that she would have searched for someone willing to help her. She was beginning to realise that, despite everything, she wasn't that eager to end her marriage, even if her common sense told her that her chances of finding permanent happiness with Alex were slim.

Madame glanced at her pale face closely but curbed her obvious curiosity and merely asked, 'Did you enjoy meeting Stefan Palides and his daughter, last night?'

'They seem very pleasant,' Lisa replied politely.

'You won't know many people in Greece, I suppose,' Madame said thoughtfully. 'You and Alex must have mutual friends in London, though, especially as you were married to Philip Fielding.'

Lisa glanced at her quickly. Was Madame trying to tell her something, rather than just making simple conversation? Being Alex's aunt, it was unlikely that she didn't know there had been no love lost between him and Philip. Was Madame, for some obscure reason, attempting to discover the extent of the enmity that had existed between the two men?

Not being exactly sure what lay behind Madame's seemingly idle comments, she replied haltingly. 'I didn't

meet Alex until after Philip died and though they do
seem to have moved in the same circles, I don't think
they were ever close friends. Philip, of course, was much
older than Alex.'

'Alex has many close friends much older than your
late husband,' Madame said drily.

Lisa sighed, still not quite sure what Madame was
getting at or if, indeed, she was getting at anything. Yet
she could have sworn there was something. 'I think
whatever it was that caused the ill-feeling between them
must have happened before my time.'

'Where did you and Alex meet, my child? He has told
me very little.'

Lisa hesitated then, unconsciously encouraged by
Madame's kinder tones, replied slowly, 'When Philip
died he left me the island of Enos. You've probably
heard of it or even know it, as it once belonged to Alex
and I think either he or his family must have lived
there. Anyway, it was Philip's last wish, apparently, that
I should sell it to Alex.'

Madame nodded and stared at Lisa narrowly for a
few long seconds. 'Did either of them tell you why?'

'No.' Lisa shook her head. 'Have you any idea?'

'Haven't you asked Alex?'

Lisa had but without success. Admittedly she hadn't
asked him about Enos since they had been married, but
if Alex had wanted to tell her about it, wouldn't he have
done so voluntarily?

'I did ask him to tell me about it in the beginning,'
she confessed. 'In fact I was so curious about it that I
said I wouldn't let him have it unless he did, but he
refused to even discuss it.'

'Yet you let him have it?'

'Yes.'

Madame frowned. 'I won't ask what kind of
persuasion he used. Alex isn't too scrupulous when it
comes to getting his own way.'

Lisa's cheeks coloured. 'I had no intention of keeping

the island. At least,' she admitted, rather startled by the resentment she felt at Madame's slight criticism of Alex and trying to be unbiased, 'not after I saw for myself how impossible it would be. Before that I had been wondering if I couldn't live there, but as soon as I saw it I realised I could never have afforded to live there, even modestly. The house is in ruins and the island resembles a fortress more than anything else.'

'It was originally bought because of that,' Madame revealed. 'My brother and sister-in-law lived there largely for that reason. Tell me,' she asked, with the frankness Lisa was coming to expect from her, 'why did someone like you marry Philip Fielding? You are obviously young enough to have been his daughter and hardly likely to have been in love with him, but, since Alex brought you here, I've been watching you closely and can't believe you would marry him for his money?'

'I didn't.' Lisa bit her lip. Madame had told her one or two things she hadn't known and was much more sympathetic than she had at first thought. Suddenly she longed to confide in her yet she wasn't sure how much she dared tell her. She hadn't even told Alex the truth about her marriage. She had tried to, of course, but he had refused to listen. He had been too busy condemning her. It made her feel bitter that his aunt, who had only known her a few days, should have so much more faith in her.

'It's kind of you to give me the benefit of the doubt,' she went on, with a faint sigh which betrayed more than her words did. 'You were quite right, I didn't love Philip but I can't honestly say I didn't marry him for his money . . .' Unhappily she explained what had taken place. 'My mother would have objected very strongly,' she finished, 'but she was so ill that it was fairly easy to disguise the truth. If my father hadn't loved her so much I don't think he would have allowed me to go through with it.'

'Even so,' Madame said drily, 'I'm surprised that he did.'

'I never held it against him,' Lisa said quickly. 'Remember,' her voice faltered, 'it was my mother as well as his wife, and Philip did assure him it was only a business arrangement. He had Edward Sterne draw up a proper agreement so nothing could go wrong.'

'Edward Sterne?' Madame sniffed derisively. 'Somehow I can't believe he would believe that, but I can imagine he would do his best to protect you.'

'He's been a good friend.' Lisa blinked to hide the foolish tears in her eyes. 'How well do you know him?'

'Probably as well as I knew your late husband,' Madame replied evasively. 'I hope Philip treated you well?'

'He never attempted to break the agreement, if that's what you mean, but I couldn't help feeling relieved when I was free again.'

Madame's eyes grew keener. 'Yet you married again and your second marriage isn't going well, either.'

'Not—very,' Lisa admitted, her white face revealing some of the misery she was trying to hide.

Madame's face softened as she leaned forward to pat her hand. 'But you love my nephew.'

'More than I ever thought I could love anyone,' Lisa confessed huskily, 'but he doesn't love me.'

Madame frowned. 'I wish I could say you're mistaken but I can never be sure what Alex is thinking. I'm convinced though that he has some very strong feelings for you. He has known plenty of women but has never married one before.'

'He was going to though,' Lisa whispered.

'Ah, you mean Letha?' Madame allowed herself a slight smile. 'Her father would have approved of such a union between his daughter and Alex, but Alex didn't appear to share his enthusiasm.'

Lisa didn't find Madame's statement as comforting as perhaps she intended it to be. Alex would have married eventually. He wanted sons and would consider it his duty to ensure the continuance of his family name, especially when he had no brothers or sisters. Lisa suspected she was the one last indulgence he was allowing himself before he settled down seriously.

To her mixed relief and dismay, before Madame could continue the conversation, which was becoming painful, Alex appeared.

'Any coffee going spare?' he asked, sitting down beside them.

'Plenty.' Reaching for the silver coffee pot, Lisa tried to reply as lightly. If Alex was determined to pretend nothing was wrong, then, for his aunt's sake, she felt bound to support him. Madame might realise it was just a front but Lisa was sure she would be the first to agree it was more comfortable than open warfare.

Knowing that Madame was aware of the strained atmosphere between them, Lisa was surprised when, after a few minutes' introspective silence, she suggested that Alex spent the rest of the morning showing Lisa something of the island.

Alex frowned and agreed though he set his cup down with a bang which implied he didn't care for such interference. Lisa, her cheeks hot with humiliation at his obvious reluctance, insisted there was no need.

'There's every need!' Madame said tartly. 'You can't burden me with the task of entertaining your bride, Alex. I'm an old woman and you know how talking tires me.'

Alex's frown deepened, as if he knew no such thing, but he rose and drew Lisa to her feet and set off without further argument.

He took her to the village, ignoring her protests, and while Lisa felt warmed by the people who greeted them from all sides, she wasn't surprised that she didn't enjoy herself.

Eventually Alex chose to notice her strained expression. 'You clearly hate being with me,' he said tersely, 'so let's get back before it becomes apparent to everyone.'

'It won't be long before they all know,' she replied unsteadily, as he almost threw her into the tough utility he drove, which was able to negotiate the rough island roads.

He didn't reply until they reached the house and he pulled into the dark overhang of the garage. 'Seriously, Lisa, I don't see why anyone should know anything. At least,' he added thickly, 'not for a long time. I realise you are sulking over the contract but it shouldn't be impossible to put it out of your mind.' He turned to her with a muttered exclamation and pulled her into his arms. 'I can't bear seeing you upset, my darling, especially when there's no need.'

Bitterly, as she huddled against him, Lisa wished she could follow his advice. Under the circumstances he probably wasn't demanding anything unreasonable, only neither of them had allowed for her mounting aversion to a marriage based entirely on sex. This, which she found impossible to explain to him, was something he didn't seem to understand.

Stubbornly she refused to look at him even while every bone in her body longed to respond to him. She could feel an urgency in him, bordering on desperation which bewildered and even frightened her. It was this quick fear of something she couldn't define which made her ignore his taut but tender tones and lash back at him wildly.

'If you really felt disturbed over seeing me upset, you would leave me alone and stay out of my bed.'

Alex stiffened, his gentler expression changing to one of coldness. Suddenly he thrust her from him, as if he could no longer bear to touch her. 'If that's what you really want,' he said tightly, 'consider your wish granted.' Rage leapt from his eyes, directed straight at her. 'God knows I've tried just about everything except going down on my knees, and that I won't do. I just can't figure you out, Lisa, but if you want to be left alone then I'll oblige. Only don't complain when you feel lonely. I thought ... Oh hell,' he shrugged, 'what does it matter what I thought, but I won't force myself on you. If I ever make love to you again it will be because you come to me and beg, but by then I'll have probably lost interest.'

Slamming out of the vehicle, his dark face more incensed than she had ever seen it, he strode from the garage. Lisa watched him going, dazed shock in her eyes, a sinking feeling in her stomach as the rigid lines of his powerful shoulders assured her he wouldn't be back. Metaphorically, he might only be going as far as his study but as far as she was concerned it might as well be the other side of the world. He would become a virtual stranger, no longer prepared to coax and kiss her or bully her into what she scarcely dared admit had been glorious submission.

But wasn't this what she wanted? She was still asking herself this after spending a miserable day without him. Contrary to her belief, he hadn't gone to his study but out on his boat after leaving her. She had watched him sailing out to sea, a hard lump in her throat that was still there twelve hours later. She had dressed with care for dinner, wearing her most attractive dress and arranging her hair exactly how he liked it, but the extra effort had seemed wasted when he didn't return.

This was bad enough but when time passed and there was no sign of him she began to worry. For all Madame assured her that Alex often went off by himself like this, she had a terrible fear that something might have happened to him. Every story she had ever read about tragedies at sea returned to haunt her and the next morning found her with dark shadows under her eyes and a white, strained face which no amount of make-up was able to disguise.

Determined to control the terrible anxiety that was eating away at her, she went for a long walk along the shore, but after breakfast, with little to occupy her, she slipped into a brooding sadness which deepened into depression as hour followed hour with no word from him.

It was after lunch before he returned and merely nodded abruptly to Lisa and his aunt, who were just leaving the dining room, before going into his study. He looked fit and tanned but so unapproachable that Lisa found she didn't dare speak to him. She tried to hide the tears of relief in her eyes but she knew Madame saw them.

'Alex is in one of his black moods,' Madeline observed indifferently. 'If I were you, my child,' she advised, as Lisa took an involuntary step towards the study door, 'I'd leave him to come out of it. No use exposing yourself to more strain than necessary.'

'I—I said some awful things to him, Madame,' Lisa confessed brokenly. 'I'm not sure that he will ever forgive me . . .'

'Would it matter?'

Lisa felt pain searing through her as she followed Madame to the lounge for coffee. Madame had kept her distance since her bewildering change of attitude yesterday. Lisa felt wary of confiding in her again yet her despair was greater than her pride.

'You know it would,' she whispered. 'I love Alex and, when I'm horrible to him, I find I hurt him less than I do myself.'

'Maybe the time has come for you to meet each other halfway,' Madame said enigmatically, as a maid followed them in with the coffee tray.

Madame seemed to be uttering more than the usual hackneyed cliché but Lisa felt too dispirited to ask what she meant and, as Madeline didn't say anything more, they drank their coffee in silence. It was later, as Madame was announcing it was time for her afternoon nap, that Alex came in.

Lisa glanced at him quickly then away again, for fear

she burst into tears, but, when he spoke, her eyes flew back to his face.

'I have to go to Athens, Lisa,' he said curtly. 'Paul will be picking me up in a couple of hours and I want you to come with me.'

She heard Madame ask quickly, as if trying to give her time to think before she replied, 'Nothing serious, I hope, Alex?'

He merely shrugged. 'Can you be ready, Lisa? You won't need much.'

She nodded numbly, realising she had no choice but to comply. Madame might be trying to help her but there was little she could do. Alex must have done a lot of thinking while he had been away. He must intend taking her to Athens and leaving her there and returning to Sanara alone. He looked so unforgiving that she was sure she was right.

When Paul arrived she was ready, having only packed a small overnight bag and changed into a pair of cotton slacks which she thought might be more practical for flying. The rest of her things, Alex would have to dispose of as he saw fit. She couldn't bear to pack any of the beautiful gowns he had bought her. They would remind her too poignantly of a honeymoon which had never really got off the ground.

She said goodbye to Madame quickly but as Madeline seemed to have no inkling of her nephew's intentions, their parting was relatively smooth.

'You'll probably be back some time tomorrow,' she smiled. 'And remember what I told you.'

Madame had told Lisa so much that she didn't even begin trying to remember, as she sat beside Alex on the helicopter. Paul was at the controls. He had flown in half an hour ago, which was all Alex had allowed him, so anxious was he to be off.

On the aircraft it was too noisy to talk easily but, for once, Lisa was glad. She and Alex could have little to say to each other and idle conversation would be pointless. Weak tears filled her eyes and she passed a hand over her face quickly, trying to blink the moisture away, and was dismayed to find a spotless hankerchief dropped in her lap.

Unhappily she used it but without gratitude. Alex would be only concerned that Paul might notice her tears and wonder about them. Yet, on giving the handkerchief back to him, she was surprised to see how tense he looked. She could never recall seeing him quite so uptight before. He took power and success so much for granted that he didn't seem vulnerable to the ordinary emotions which attacked other men. In London he had been exuberant and expansive and though much more complex than she had at first imagined, certainly not given to the kind of tension which seemed to be attacking him now.

Still, it wouldn't be every day he disposed of a wife! He wouldn't be the first man to find the trauma of it maybe more than he'd bargained for. Trying to drown ever threatening tears beneath a deluge of cynicism, Lisa closed her eyes and determined to keep them closed until they reached Athens.

She must have dozed off for she woke to find they had landed without being aware that the engines had stopped.

'Alex?' she breathed, sitting up abruptly on finding him shaking her gently. 'I didn't realise . . .'

'You fell asleep.'

She was too busy hiding her confusion to look around. She didn't do this until he had helped her to the ground. It wasn't until then that she saw, with stunned surprise, that they were on Enos. She recognised the wild and rugged terrain immediately and wondered why they had called here.

'Alex?' she exclaimed. 'Why aren't we in Athens?'

'Not just now, darling,' he muttered, as Paul dropped two sacks from the helicopter, practically on top of them and he thrust her out of the way. 'About twelve, tomorrow,' he shouted to Paul as he dragged the sacks aside and gave him a careless wave.

Lisa failed to find her voice until the helicopter was a mere speck in the sky. Turning to Alex, her face pale with tension, she whispered, 'Will you please explain?'

He stared down at the sacks he was holding for several seconds before he raised his head and looked at her. 'I don't know that I can, not logically anyway. I brought you here because I believe we have to talk. Well,' he conceded, a faint tinge of red in his cheeks, 'that's one of the reasons—the rest probably depends on what we talk about.'

Lisa's heart was beating so painfully she could scarcely think, much less talk. 'Wouldn't your apartment in Athens have done just as well? After all, the only thing we have to discuss is a divorce.'

He winced and she noticed for the first time the lines of strain in his face. Beneath the sea-tan he had acquired, he was really quite pale. Even his black eyes, which usually gleamed and glowed like those of a superior, prowling tiger, were opaque, as if some emotion lingering behind them was torturing him.

'I didn't bring you here to discuss a divorce,' he said tonelessly. 'Let's get this lot up to the house first.'

Picking up the small things he couldn't carry, Lisa had no other option but to stumble after him. 'You must be crazy!' she gasped, catching up with him.

'Possibly,' he agreed. 'I've been going slowly insane ever since I met you.'

Lisa gulped as this sounded far from flattering. 'Do you intend us to sleep out, like we did the first time?'

'Yes,' he snapped, lengthening his stride as if even the mention of that first time angered him.

Owing to the rate Alex was travelling, the house soon came in view. Lisa was panting so hard trying to keep up with him, she hadn't time to sort out the turmoil of her thoughts. If Alex wasn't going to talk about divorce, what had he in mind? Was he simply going to murder her to save himself the bother? A man in his position could probably get away with it.

By the time he dropped the sacks in exactly the same spot where they had camped before, Lisa had managed somehow to convince herself that Alex wasn't the type to stoop to murder, but she was still no nearer to finding a solution.

Turning to her, Alex said, 'If you would unpack, I'll build a fire, but before we eat I'd like to show you over the island. You refused to come with me when we were here before but I'd like you to see it.'

Lisa's fingers seemed all thumbs as she obeyed him. What did Alex want with her? He said he wanted to talk but what could he have to say that she would want to hear? And there would be a long night to get through after that. Another night, like the previous one, when she hadn't been able to sleep, might be more than she could stand. Alex would be nearer to her tonight, she wouldn't have the worry of wondering if he was lost at sea, but in every other way he would be just as distant.

Moving numbly, she laid out the sleeping bags and placed a picnic basket, containing numerous flasks, which she supposed held their dinner beside them. She hoped someone was going to be hungry enough to enjoy it. Alex, she noticed, had lit the fire within the perimeter of flat stones left from the last time, and gone to the well to fetch a kettle of water.

She flinched when she thought of the well and was relieved when he returned and asked if she was ready. When she nodded, he wedged the kettle between two of the stones, where it would heat slowly while they were away.

For a while they trudged in silence. A slight breeze sprang up, blowing Lisa's wealth of fair hair back in silky waves from the delicate perfection of her face. She felt Alex's eyes on her and shivered to realise how every inch of her body reacted to exactly the precise moment his glance passed over it. Chemistry, she scorned fiercely, wishing miserably that she could have experienced it with any other man but him!

Because she didn't want her feelings for Alex to get the better of her, she tried to concentrate on the island. Soon, as they tramped over the barren, rockstrewn ground, she became even more dismayed by the extreme starkness of it than she had been. When she had seen it before she had thought it bleak and inhospitable. Today she saw nothing to make her change her mind.

'What do you think of it?' Alex asked abruptly, when they returned to the house.

'I'm not sure,' she replied hesitantly. 'But,' she confessed ruefully, 'I'm rather glad I didn't decide to keep it. I think it would take a special kind of person to live here.'

'Yet you like Sanara and that is fairly primitive and isolated.'

'Not like this, though,' she retorted. 'Enos is so bleak, I think I would feel cold here even on the warmest day.'

He glanced at her sharply as she stood despondently by the campfire. 'That is exactly how I felt when I was a boy.'

Lisa frowned. No wonder he was so tough and self-sufficient if he'd grown up here. 'Did you live here for long periods?' she heard herself asking.

'I went to boarding school when I was eight, and finished up in one of your famous universities, so I suppose it was only for holidays but, until my father died, this was considered the family home.'

Alex had never mentioned his childhood before and had refused to talk about the island. A few weeks ago, she would have welcomed hearing every small detail, but now she wasn't so sure. Hadn't she enough to forget as it was? Almost fearfully she stared at him, wondering if she would manage to forget anything.

'I'm not about to attack you,' Alex said tersely, meeting her apprehensive eyes.

'I didn't think you were . . .'

'Then relax, sit down.'

Rather than explain what she had been worrying about, she chose a soft clump of grass near the fire and did as she was told. 'Do you really intend staying here overnight?' she asked uncertaintly.

'Yes.' He passed her a cup of coffee and she was glad he hadn't begun serving dinner. The coffee eased the tension in her throat but she didn't think she could have swallowed anything solid.

Alex stirred sugar in his cup then said suddenly, 'Madeline rang Edward Sterne yesterday morning. That was why she wanted us out of the way.'

Lisa was immediately filled with inexplicable panic but she managed to murmur lightly, 'Why should Madame do that?'

'She wanted him to speak to me. I suspected she was up to something but after what happened in the garage, I only wanted to get away.'

Lisa gazed at the ground in front of her, not wanting him to guess how much she had suffered through his absence and had felt punished by the things she had said to him. Unsteadily she enquired, 'Did Madame tell you this?'

'No,' he replied curtly. 'I probably wouldn't have known if Edward hadn't let something slip. It's not like him, I realise, but he had been trying to contact me for over twenty-four hours and was in a bit of a state.'

'Edward was . . .?' She had sent him word that she was getting married, and he had replied that he was delighted. Lisa lifted widening eyes to her husband's face, neither Madeline's actions nor Edward's making sense.

As Lisa gazed at him, seemingly at loss, he said heavily, 'I may as well confess, Lisa, that after speaking to Sterne and realising what a fool I'd been, I wanted to tell you—talk to you, somewhere where you couldn't escape listening. This was partly why I thought of Enos, but now I'm not so sure it was such a good idea, after all.' His face hardened bitterly. 'I'd give my right arm,

Lisa, to be able to say I believed in you without proof, but now that's impossible.'

'What has Edward been saying to you?' Lisa exclaimed anxiously, bewildered by the torment in his eyes and wishing she could do something to alleviate it. She had an overwhelming desire to put her arms around him and comfort him but she sensed his struggle to keep his distance and respected it.

'God, Lisa!' He prowled restlessly. 'It makes me feel a heel to know that my aunt, who only met you two days ago, believed in you while I didn't. When Edward told me you'd married Fielding solely for the sake of your parents, and what sort of a marriage you'd had, I could have killed myself for having had so little faith in you. I can't expect you to even consider forgiving me, this is why I'm beginning to realise the crass mistake I've made in bringing you here.'

Lisa watched him mutely as he paced back and forth, her feelings chaotic. She had never seen Alex like this and the harsh misery in his face shocked her. She suddenly knew, that whatever the outcome of this evening might be, she hated seeing him any other way other than as she had always known him.

It came to her too, that she might have made mistakes, as well as Alex. If he hadn't believed in her, wasn't she guilty of a similar sin? She hadn't trusted him enough to tell him the truth—she had sulked behind her pride, silently outraged by his lack of blind faith in her, when she had committed just as unreasonable a crime against him.

Lisa drew a deep breath. Now that she must confess her own shortcomings, as he had done, she didn't find it so easy. But wasn't this what Madame must have meant when she had suggested she met him halfway?

'I didn't trust you either,' she admitted, going to him and laying a trembling hand on his arm. 'It wouldn't have been impossible to have taken you to Edward's office and shown you the agreement he arranged between Philip and my parents, but I was too stubborn. You don't love me but I loved you, which makes my behaviour even less excusable.'

'Lisa?' Alex's whole body was tense as he stared down into her unhappy eyes. 'You told me you loved me once before, then changed your mind . . .'

'I never stopped loving you,' she whispered. 'It was my terrible pride . . .'

'Oh, my darling!' he exclaimed huskily, then suddenly, as if he couldn't help himself, his arms went around her in a grip that hurt, his powerful body trapping her fully as he brought his firm, sensual lips hard down on hers, once more gloriously dominant. The kiss went on and on, until she had her arms around his neck and was kissing him back, and it changed for both of them into something like a miracle.

'You love me, too,' she breathed, as he eventually lifted his dark head and gazed at her with brilliant eyes, which confirmed her statement without a need for words.

'I love you,' he muttered thickly, 'if only for believing I couldn't kiss you like that unless I did. I think I've loved you since I first saw you.' When Lisa's brows rose in teasing doubt, he confessed ironically. 'If it didn't seem that way, it was because I was fighting it, but it was a hopeless battle.'

'Why did you fight it?' she asked curiously. 'Unless,' she bit her lip, 'you really wished to marry Letha?'

'Never,' he denied emphatically. 'I merely pretended I had her in mind to try and defend myself against you.'

'Then it must have been my reputation,' she said hollowly.

'Lisa!' His mouth tightening as she went pale again, he lowered her swiftly to one of the sleeping bags, then sat beside her, keeping his arms around her. 'I've still a lot of explaining to do but I'm almost frightened to begin, for fear you don't understand.'

'Try me,' she suggested tremulously.

He frowned and was silent a few moments before he began, as if he was searching for the right words. 'I was born here,' he said at last. 'This was really why I brought you here, today. I thought the harshness of the island might help you to understand the way I'm made. Until I was eight, I spent all my time on Enos with only my mother and the servants for company. This was why, I suppose, I always felt close to her and tried to respect her last wishes which had, indirectly, to do with you.'

'But I never knew your mother.' Lisa frowned.

'I know you didn't,' he said. 'Her last wishes had nothing to do with you, personally, but you see, when she was young, Philip Fielding wanted to marry her.'

Lisa still wasn't following. 'Philip . . . did?'

'Yes. She became an obsession with him apparently, and when she rejected him for my father, he never forgot or forgave her. I didn't learn any of this until he won Enos from me in a game of cards.'

'You gambled on the island?'

'I was twenty,' he said wryly, 'and brash. Too full of my own importance, I imagine, to believe I wasn't invincible. This was what my egoism wouldn't allow me to confess to you, even fifteen years later. Philip had still kept in touch with my family through business and probably didn't find it too difficult to get me in his company that night and load me with drink. What followed was inevitable. He got Enos.'

'But—didn't it belong to your father?' Lisa asked uncertainly.

Alex's lips twisted. 'He had died, leaving it to me. He wanted me to have it and obviously assumed that if my mother married again I might lose it.'

'Did she?'

'No.' His eyes went bleak. 'She died within a few years of having to leave here. I always felt guilty but she blamed Fielding. She begged me never to have anything more to do with him, or anything that belonged to him.'

'And you promised?' Lisa's voice was strained.

He shook his head, his arms tightening as he sensed her dismay. Neither of us thought that was necessary. I didn't plan on having anything more to do with him and never changed my mind, not even in recent years when I've occasionally been in a position to ruin him. He had promised I should have Enos back after he died, but though I pretended to you I had expected it, nothing could have been further from the truth. When you turned up in Athens, I felt I'd been hit by something hard in the stomach, but what I took for dislike, I soon realised was quite the opposite. Knowing you were Philip's widow, though, put you out of bounds. I kept remembering my mother, as well as your supposed reputation. When I found it impossible to fight my desire for you, I decided to make you my mistress. I believed this would be one way of squaring with my conscience and getting what I wanted.'

Lisa shivered, feeling cold and shocked. 'Since then you married me,' she choked. 'What about your conscience now?'

One of his hands caressed the pale outline of her face tenderly then he pulled her to him with a muffled groan. 'I admit I grabbed at the excuse to marry you, my darling. A face-saving exercise, I suppose, for I had known for some time it would come to that. You are far more important to me than anyone else, either living or dead. When you talked of leaving me I was shattered for despite everything I'd said, I knew I could never give you up. And that was before I discovered there was nothing about you that could have possibly offended my mother. She would have loved you, I know.'

'I wish I had known her,' Lisa said wistfully, aware of a sudden happiness stirring inside her. 'What was she like?'

'Very sweet and gentle,' he kissed her softly, 'like you.'

'Then she wouldn't have been happy with Philip,'

Lisa frowned, wrapping her arms about his neck. 'He once told me,' she recalled, 'how he had only loved two women in his entire life. One was Gilda but he never named the other one.'

'It's a funny kind of love that seeks only revenge,' Alex said soberly. 'Although he may have tried to make amends and, if nothing else, was responsible for our meeting.'

'What will you do with the island now, Alex?' she asked anxiously.

'Pull the house down, perhaps, and leave it as a kind of shrine to my parents. No one else would wish to live here.'

'Where will we live?' she asked, with a sudden shy radiance which told him she intended living with him forever.

'Sanara, mostly,' he said thickly, his fingers busy unbuttoning her shirt. 'First, though, we are going to have at least three months' honeymoon in an idyllic spot in the Pacific, where I hope to convince you how much I love you and how sorry I am for the despicable way I've treated you.'

'I've forgotten already,' she assured him.

'Oh, my darling,' he murmured, his hands still, the pain in his voice making her press a swift kiss on his cheek. 'I've been a brute and a fool, threatening you with stupid contracts and divorce, I can't expect to be forgiven that easily.'

In a voice husky with emotion, she whispered against his lips. 'What happiness would I ever find if I didn't? And life without you wouldn't be worth living.'

His eyes glowed with the love he had been denying for weeks as he held her tightly in his hard arms. 'I've discovered a whole new set of emotions since meeting you,' he growled. 'Not just lust,' he reproved as her soft mouth quirked teasingly, 'though you make everything I've ever known with other women seem luke-warm. I want to look after you, protect you. I feel a soul-shaking tenderness for you that I've never felt before. The only time I ever felt anything like it was for a puppy I once owned.'

'So now you're comparing me with a dog!'

'Young woman!' he retorted severely. 'If you knew the adoration a young boy can feel for his puppy, you wouldn't complain.'

'So,' she said innocently, 'first it's your other women, then your . . . Oh!' she gasped, as he lowered her so swiftly to the ground that the breath was almost knocked out of her, especially when he covered her with his powerful body.

'If my talking doesn't please you,' he muttered, after kissing her thoroughly, 'let's see what else will. Only,' he added softly, after another long silence, during which his hands were as busy as his lips, 'after depriving me of my rights, last night, you'd better be prepared to make up for it.'

Lisa hugged him to her with fervent compliance, aware that she was deeply content. Alex and she had been through a lot and she had never expected to find such happiness. Passionately she pressed her slender body against his, as his hands caressed her, knowing that what they had was so strong and endurable that nothing could destroy it. When he gripped her fiercely, his possession swift and eager, Lisa felt her body expanding as she responded to his demanding hunger.

'I love you,' she whispered as the world about them exploded.

'Not as much as I love you,' her husband breathed, a long time later.

Take 4
Exciting Books
Absolutely
FREE

Love, romance, intrigue... all are captured for you by Mills & Boon's top-selling authors. By becoming a regular reader of Mills & Boon's Romances you can enjoy 6 superb new titles every month plus a whole range of special benefits: your very own personal membership card, a free monthly newsletter packed with recipes, competitions, exclusive book offers and a monthly guide to the stars, plus extra bargain offers and big cash savings.

AND an Introductory FREE GIFT for YOU.
Turn over the page for details.

As a special introduction we will send you four exciting Mills & Boon Romances Free and without obligation when you complete and return this coupon.

At the same time we will reserve a subscription to Mills & Boon Reader Service for you. Every month, you will receive 6 of the very latest novels by leading Romantic Fiction authors, delivered direct to your door. You don't pay extra for delivery — postage and packing is always completely Free. There is no obligation or commitment — you can cancel your subscription at any time.

You have nothing to lose and a whole world of romance to gain.

Just fill in and post the coupon today to **MILLS & BOON READER SERVICE, FREEPOST, P.O. BOX 236, CROYDON, SURREY CR9 9EL.**

Please Note:- READERS IN SOUTH AFRICA write to Mills & Boon, Postbag X3010, Randburg 2125, S. Africa.

FREE BOOKS CERTIFICATE

To: Mills & Boon Reader Service, FREEPOST, P.O. Box 236, Croydon, Surrey CR9 9EL.

Please send me, free and without obligation, four Mills & Boon Romances, and reserve a Reader Service Subscription for me. If I decide to subscribe I shall, from the beginning of the month following my free parcel of books, receive six new books each month for £6.60, post and packing free. If I decide not to subscribe, I shall write to you within 10 days The free books are mine to keep in any case. I understand that I may cancel my subscription at any time simply by writing to you. I am over 18 years of age.

Please write in BLOCK CAPITALS.

Signature _____

Name _____

Address _____

_____ Post code _____

SEND NO MONEY — TAKE NO RISKS.

Please don't forget to include your Postcode.

Remember, postcodes speed delivery. Offer applies in UK only and is not valid to present subscribers. Mills & Boon reserve the right to exercise discretion in granting membership. If price changes are necessary you will be notified.

6R   Offer expires 31st March 1986.

EP8